P9-DGJ-039

INTEGRATED BALANCE TRAINING

• • • • •

A PROGRAMMING GUIDE

FOR

FITNESS AND HEALTH PROFESSIONALS

• • • • •

• • • • •

BY DOUGLAS BROOKS M.S.

AND

CANDICE COPELAND BROOKS

©Copyright 2002 DW Fitness, LLC

All rights reserved.

Reproduction of this work in any form, including Xerography, photocopying or any other type of copying or recording is forbidden without the written permission of DW Fitness, LLC.

No manual or book can replace the services of a trained physician, exercise physiologist or other qualified health or exercise professional. Any application of the information set forth in the following pages is at the reader's discretion and sole risk.

ISBN #1-878655-09-4

Photography: John Formanek
Page Design: Barbara Blohm
Cover Design: Lucia Formanek
BOSU Inventor: David Weck
BOSU Programming Developed by: Douglas Brooks, M.S., Jennifer Cole, Candice Copeland Brooks and David Weck

For more information on BOSU videos and programming manuals, please contact:
www.BOSUpro.com, or www.MovesIntFitness.com

BOSU® is a registered trademark of DW Fitness, LLC.

TABLE OF CONTENTS

· · · · ·

BOSU INTEGRATED BALANCE TRAINING EXERCISES

WHAT IS BOSU?

BOSU is an acronym for "both sides up." The BOSU Balance Trainer can be used with the platform side either up or down for different types of balance challenge. The solid platform is 25 inches in diameter and the dome should be inflated until it is firm. Two recessed handles on the bottom of, and toward the sides of the platform make it easy to turn over or carry. This hybrid fitness product has its genesis in the field of medicine, as well as balance, functional and sport specific training. Neuromuscular physiology, which helps to define human movement, provides the science that backs this complete approach to training. It is accurate to say that the BOSU Balance Trainer offers a different means to make exercise more appealing and effective for average people, fitness enthusiasts and highly trained athletes.

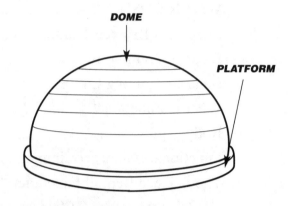

TOP SIDE OF BOSU

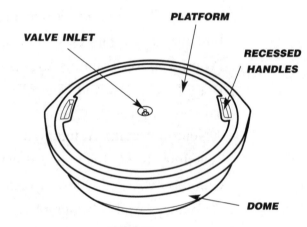

UNDER SIDE OF BOSU

INTEGRATED BALANCE TRAINING

The BOSU Balance Trainer is a truly unique balance, core stability and proprioception training device that can be integrated with all types of fitness training, or stand alone as an outstanding, functional conditioning tool. The BOSU can be used for or with:

- Sports conditioning, aerobic and anaerobic training

- Stabilization, balance and agility training

- Strength, stability and flexibility training for the trunk

- Strength, stability and flexibility training for the entire body

- Existing fitness programming

- Other fitness training equipment

INTEGRATING BALANCE WITH CARDIOVASCULAR TRAINING

While exercising on the BOSU Balance Trainer you can walk, run, step, hop, jump and leap. Not only can these rhythmic activities be sequenced for an aerobic workout, they can be progressed or sequenced to challenge the anaerobic energy system as well. Whether you're working at an easy "steady-rate" pace that can be maintained almost indefinitely, or pushing the intensity with anaerobic intervals, you'll experience dynamic balance and stabilization challenges. This type of training replicates the "real" aspect of sport and daily movement requirements, where cardiovascular training transfers to real-life movement. Challenging the body's oxygen delivery and utilization (VO2) capability is not only effective on BOSU, but the added elements of fun, stabilization, balance challenge and specific transfer to daily movement needs will make this type of training a favorite.

INTEGRATING BALANCE WITH MUSCULAR ENDURANCE AND STRENGTH TRAINING

Targeted muscular endurance and strength exercises can be performed effectively on the BOSU Balance Trainer. Your ability to sustain moderate to high levels of muscular force production will be enhanced through a variety of dynamic and static movements. The entire strength continuum, which ranges from low-level muscular endurance through maximal strength and power, can be trained while integrating balance and stabilization. Using many different exercises, which incorporate balance and stabilization, you will develop functional muscular power, and strength and endurance, while simultaneously training and coordinating your balance reactions.

INTEGRATING BALANCE WITH FLEXIBILITY TRAINING

Both active and passive stretches can be taught on BOSU, with balance assistance and/or balance challenges. Active stretches use the muscles of the body to move a body part, whereas passive stretching uses gravity or an outside force to put stretch-tension on the target muscle(s). While standing or kneeling on the dome, an active and dynamic stretch is exemplified by moving the upper body lower, higher, to the side, or can be created by reaching for and picking up cards from various locations on the floor, or by touching and/or relocating cones that have been placed in close proximity to the dome. Stretching on the BOSU can move from a static and passive approach, to a dynamic, balance challenging and active approach.

INTEGRATING BALANCE WITH SPORTS CONDITIONING

Sports conditioning, by nature, is dynamic. The qualities of sports movement that can be trained with BOSU include muscular strength, endurance and power, cardiovascular conditioning, agility, balance, proprioception and flexibility. Through a variety of static balance exercises (i.e., stand on one leg), and dynamic balance drills (jump vertically and stick a landing on top of the dome), what you can accomplish with regard to specific transfer to virtually any sport, is almost unlimited. One, two or multiple BOSUs can be used to set up drill patterns for sport or recreational activity goals.

INTEGRATING BALANCE WITH CORE TRAINING

Both core stabilization and mover- or isolation-type trunk conditioning can take place in a variety of positions on the BOSU Balance Trainer. The abs can work functionally in standing, kneeling, seated, sidelying, prone and supine positions, and can be challenged with traditional isolation exercises, or stabilization exercises, where the goal of the exercise is to maintain a neutral and otherwise, properly aligned spine. Maintaining spinal alignment is important to low back health and sport performance, as is intentionally moving into and out of "perfect" or neutral posture.

Whether the focus is cardiovascular, strength and flexibility training – or balance, agility and sport movement – the BOSU Integrated Balance Workout integrates the concept of "body equilibrium" into a *total* fitness approach and introduces an element that could be termed "fun" or "play." A workout approach like this, teamed with a unique balance-training device, results in a training program that will improve proprioception and balance through systematic exercises and drills that are progressive and challenging.

BALANCE TRAINING BENEFITS

• • • • •

BOSU exercises challenge both your mind and body to participate in order to sustain correct posture and balance. Training on the BOSU requires you to *maintain* your center of gravity over a dynamic, ever changing surface that is created by the air-filled dome.

Following are some of the benefits that can be expected from balance training:

• Balance training will enhance coordination, balance and neuromuscular function. From rehabilitation and daily movement requirements, to enhancement of functional movement and sports performance, balance training has specific carry-over.

• Balance training develops and keeps sensory feedback systems sharp and well trained. This translates to neuromuscular training that increases movement efficiency, regardless of the activity.

• Balance training on a dynamic, gel-like surface (such as the air-filled BOSU dome) requires a collaborative effort by your muscles, which will result in improved posture and functional movement experiences. In real-life situations, you are rarely called on to isolate musculature. Instead, balance training calls into play movers, stabilizers and counterbalancing forces that closely mimic everyday activities and tasks.

• Balance training can boost movement performance, efficiency and safety.

• Balance training will help to develop balance and stabilizing strength that will result in improved postural endurance.

• Balance training will help to eliminate neuromuscular imbalances and improve every day function.

• Balance training will create a new sense of body awareness, body positioning, postural alignment, and movement confidence.

• Balance training requires an integrated response from both the body and the mind. This type of "mindful training" results in total body, functional fitness gains.

• Balance training can introduce a sense of fun or play into a general or athletic conditioning program.

BALANCE TRAINING
CAN BE "FUN"

· · · · ·

Good things happen when you're having fun and enjoy the activity in which you participate. Steven Wright is quoted as saying, "You have to stay in shape. My mother started walking five miles a day when she was 60. She's 97 now and we have no idea where she is." You get the idea. The word *fitness* should be permanently fused to the word fun (McLaughlin, 2001).

Balance training, literally, can be a prescription for fun. Personal isolation is common in today's workplace because of the "information highway." Loneliness and depression are widespread among today's workers who sit at computers for a large portion of the day. People are generally tired, overstressed, overworked, overweight and unfit because of today's labor and time saving technology.

Not only do people need to know when to power down, but the concept of working out should be perceived as time efficient, effective and fun. Most people realize that fitness and health depend largely upon consistency and reasonable effort. While this is true, a message like this is not too

exciting or motivating. Balance training workouts are not only result oriented and efficient, but can also encourage laughter and play. Workout time moves quickly when you're focused on the task at hand, and can literally see improvement with each workout.

Goal oriented "play" is an important aspect of any results oriented program. Play is something you want to do and something you enjoy doing. Play is something you'll return to time and time again. Play is challenging and can even be hard. Play makes you feel good.

Integrated Balance Training takes movement patterns and exercises and incorporates them into a unique modular training system that helps improve proprioception and balance within *every* component of fitness, while simultaneously encouraging the aspects of non-competitive fun and fitness play.

WHAT IS FUNCTIONAL TRAINING?

· · · · ·

Generally, functional training is tied to balance training and sport-, activity-, or occupational-specific practice. Therefore, knowledge of what proprioception represents, how it relates to functional or useable movement, and why you have this "body sense" is important. But, functional training is more than just balance, stabilization or proprioceptive-type training. A very narrow view of functional training would see this type of training defined as stability training for the "core," or abdominal and back muscles. A much broader and accurate definition would portray functional training as activity that "trains movement," and would include activity that requires both static and dynamic muscular force production.

Your ability to be spatially aware of how the entire body, or a single body part, is positioned at any given moment must be developed and maintained by specific training. Of course, all humans have a degree of this awareness or proprioceptive ability, commonly referred to as proprioception. The concept of body-awareness becomes readily apparent as one observes how the nervous system develops from birth and a baby progresses from simple reflexive movements to coordinated movements such as crawling and walking.

As is true of all biological systems in the body, if these systems are not trained and continually challenged, function is lost. The age-old adage, "Use it or lose it!" certainly holds true. Categories of "system-loss" include areas related to cardiorespiratory fitness, strength, flexibility, balance *and* neural control. Many aspects of training make up what is referred to as "functional training." All of these systems can impact one another and must be trained with specific and different approaches so that each biological component that impacts health, fitness and performance is maintained at its highest possible peak. Any type of training that has specific application to real-life movement and/or sport can be labeled as "functional."

One "thing" that science can definitively tell us about training, is that if you are training "one way," you are training ineffectively. While it is impossible to identify the "best" approach to training, it is clear that a variety of science backed approaches must be used to adequately challenge all systems and movement requirements of the body. Functional training is one such line-of-attack that helps to fulfill this requirement.

THE KINETIC CHAIN AND FUNCTIONAL TRAINING

Functional movement can be readily understood if you view the body as a "kinetic chain." Kinetic refers to motion and the word chain represents the body's ability to link motion at the joints so that motion is harnessed, with an end result being skilled movement. Put succinctly, a kinetic chain represents movement that is made up of a series of joint motions and associated musculature working together (synergistically) through a multitude of planes and balance challenges.

The ability to swing a baseball bat, spike a volleyball, slam a tennis serve, perform a long jump, climb a rock, swing a golf club, drill a slap-shot while skating quickly, slam dunk a basketball or throw a javelin is a direct result of practice, drills and sport "play" that ingrain neural/motor patterns into our brains. Practice that is correct and accurate brands efficient motor patterns into our central nervous system. It becomes apparent why neurological or motor learning, as well as stability, balance and functional training, are important.

TRANSITIONING GENERAL STRENGTH TO FUNCTIONAL STRENGTH

Isolated strength, by itself, is of little practical value to skilled movement. You might ask, therefore; "Is a leg curl worthless?" The answer is an absolute, "No." But, strength that is gained in a non-specific or non-functional way is more effectively utilized if it can be "transitioned" to "movement specific" strength. For example, take strength that is gained in a traditional weight room format. A well thought out periodized plan of attack would, at some time in the strength development progression, follow this new strength acquisition with a "transitioning phase" or simultaneously develop functional fitness on "off" or recovery/restoration days. A transitioning phase(s) would begin to utilize training drills that mimic the activity in which the participant is going to take part. In the name of specificity it would, of course, also be necessary to actually practice and participate in the actual sport or activity. The point at which transitioning, or functional training, would take place would depend on the sport, time of season in relation to competition and/or the goal(s) of training.

A participant who is not looking for elite performance and instead is looking to progress or maintain a personal health and fitness program could simultaneously use traditional and functional approaches to fitness. Observe how much of the strength that is developed in the "weight room" is transferred to the person's ability to improve performance. It is apparent that some will transfer and this is a positive training experience. In fact, in sports where body weight and absolute strength influence performance greatly, the "weight room" may be preferred in terms of training priority in some phases of a periodized program. Regardless, it is wise to incorporate both functional and traditional training approaches, whether the goal is sport performance or maintaining physical independence with advancing age.

BODY EQUILIBRIUM

• • • • •

A number of components represent key building blocks that contribute to safe, effective and functional movement, as well as skilled performance. The concept of body equilibrium includes:

1. BALANCE. Balance represents an ability to stabilize and maintain a desired body position. Balance can also be thought of as correct, or efficient, positioning of a body part or the entire body.

2. KINESTHETIC SENSE. This feedback mechanism allows you to be aware of how the body is positioned at any moment. Kinesthetic or proprioceptive sense allows the body to perceive or feel movement, weight-shifts, resistance and position. To the point, kinesthetic awareness is the ability to know where your body parts are in three-dimensional space.

3. PROPRIOCEPTION. Proprioception, which overlaps with kinesthetic awareness, provides a sense of body symmetry, or necessary balance and positioning between body parts, and specifically refers to a sense of joint position. Proprioception, as mediated by sensory organs like muscle spindles that are located between muscle fibers, represents the ongoing or normal awareness of the position, balance or movement of the body or any of its parts.

Note: The term kinesthesis is used to define a person's awareness of motion or position as it pertains to his/her limbs. Proprioception is defined as one's sense of movement as it relates to movement of the body and how it is oriented in space. Today, current literature uses the terms as though they are synonymous (Plowman and Smith, 1997).

4. GRADATION OF FORCE. An ability to control muscular force production and maintain an equalized, though dynamic, position regardless of the physical task at hand, is critical to any type of human movement. Correct application of force is complex, learned and under the direct influence of neural control. The regulatory control of muscular force is referred to as "gradation of force."

These four components of body equilibrium are important to consider—and train—when used in the context of sport performance and daily movement requirements. Balance, kinesthetic sense, proprioception, body symmetry and proper force application are key aspects of any activity that requires a dynamic, integrated, coordinated and skilled response. Being able to change your center of gravity to compensate for required movement is the key to moving skillfully. Agility is the technical term for this developed sense that incorporates proprioception and balance, and allows us to move efficiently, confidently, gracefully and smoothly, while wasting little motion. The smooth fusion and training of all of these elements can represent skillful or functional movement, and reflect the athletic qualities that everyone should seek to develop.

Physical responses encompass a wide range of proficiency that can run the gamut from elite athleticism to an elderly person moving from a seated to standing position. All types of physical activity can be characterized as essential, important or critical, though the goals and desires to move in a specific manner may be very different. It is readily observed that body equilibrium requirements are quite different when various physical activities are compared, but no less important, independent of the activity being performed. For an elderly person it is highly important to train the body to maintain physical independence or avoid a fall. It is equally significant for a 20-year old woman to train to win a gold medal in slalom skiing. Maintenance of body equilibrium is important to all people.

The complete concept of body equilibrium moves beyond only "physical balance" and body awareness as it pertains to daily movement, functional fitness, stability training and posture. Body equilibrium *does* represent an awareness of the body as it is positioned during activity (kinesthetic awareness), and its development is accomplished by a variety of specific physical training methods that include traditional approaches to training, as well as introducing functional strength, balance and stability training. Additionally, complete and harmonious body equilibrium would also include a development of, and sense of being well balanced as it pertains to the "condition of the mind" and "overall feeling." In other words, being physically, emotionally and spiritually well balanced is the ultimate, long-range training goal that reflects the complete development of body equilibrium and the "individual" in each person.

• • • • •

Balance and stabilization training can simply be thought of as a position or series of positions that occur during movement, and that are maintained when opposing forces equalize one another. Little or no movement occurs at the stabilized joint(s). Applied to movement, this means that muscles on both sides of a joint(s) contribute to stabilization via a co-contraction of agonist and antagonistic muscles. Co-contraction of muscles on either side of a joint(s) contribute to a body part or body position being maintained in a desired, or intended symmetry or asymmetry. In essence, this *is* balance and represents an important aspect of functional movement and training!

On the other hand, functional balance training goes beyond contributing to skilled movement by training not only stabilizing or static muscular contributions, but also training dynamic movement patterns simultaneously. It is likely that most skilled movement of any kind simultaneously requires both stabilizing force production and bodily movement. For example, when skiing downhill or hitting a tennis ball, one part of the body, like the trunk, may require stabilizing force production, while another part of the body requires joint motion. Additionally, there will be movement requirements that call the trunk region into play as a "mover" and not as a stabilizer.

This is why it is correct to say that functional training incorporates many types of training, including functional balance training – and that is why it is important to understand that the broad umbrella of "functional training" trains movement specific to sport, recreation and daily life. It is easy to erroneously define functional training as one type of training, or as a specific type of movement (i.e., stabilization or balance), when in fact, it represents a diversified approach that integrates many different types of training into a total body development program.

We live and play in a world that is rich with constant and varying types of proprioceptive stimuli. This movement playground requires us to move and stabilize in every imaginable plane of movement. Therefore, it makes sense that an important training goal would be to transition non-specific strength and movement patterns to "real-life" movement, by making use of an effective, comprehensive functional training approach.

It is obvious that balance is the foundation upon which all movement is based. Quite simply, balance and muscle contraction (or force production, more accurately) play critical roles in every type of physical movement. All human movement depends on skeletal muscle contraction and the nervous system (Plowman and Smith 1997; McArdle et al., 1991). Training balance and muscles, which ultimately means training the nervous (neuromuscular) system, is essential since skeletal muscles will not contract unless they receive a signal from the nervous system. Balance is indeed the foundational platform for all human movement and keeps our neuromuscular system functioning at a high level.

THE SCIENCE BEHIND FUNCTIONAL BALANCE TRAINING

Functional, balance and stability training have been studied for many years and continue to be a mainstay of cutting-edge conditioning training programs. The scientific foundation behind this type of training has a long-standing history that is well researched and documented (Plowman and Smith, 1997; Wilmore and Costill, 1994; McArdle et al., 1991; Jackson, J.H., 1931).

All of us at one time or another have watched in awe as we witnessed a powerful physical feat like that of an Olympic lifter thrusting a Herculean amount of weight overhead, or we've intently watched a track and field athlete explode out of sprint blocks in an astounding rush of speed and power. We also look on in amazement as a world-class downhill skier seemingly glides effortlessly along a race course at 70 miles per hour, knowing that an incorrect body adjustment or terrain change could send the skier hurtling off course toward self-destruction. World-class gymnasts and figure skaters perform complex and difficult movements and make it look easy, as though these skills require little or no effort. Yet, we also know that the slightest mistake – loss of balance or a split-second lost sense of where the body is positioned in space – can result in movement that not only looks strained or unrehearsed, but that also can result in pain, injury or death.

Skilled movement is epitomized by athletes like these who perform tasks requiring complex degrees of coordination, balance, strength and power – and make them look easy! That is why we are compelled to watch the Olympics, World Cup competitions and professional athletes, in general. We especially respect skilled movement when we have experienced the simplest of gymnastic movements, or the most fundamental

aspects of skiing or other sports. Why? Because, most of us are humbled by the effort, skill, time and patience required for us to become proficient. What is one person's "fun," can be another's personal horror. Is it skill, strength, genetics or all three that set athletes apart and make fear relative? All of these variables represent the "stuff" of which sport and recreation are made, regardless of the level at which you participate. The beauty of sport and movement is that most people can experience some sense of grace, strength, power, fearlessness and improved skill.

Yet, none of this happens without a "sharp" neuromuscular system, which only occurs with practice, rehearsal, training and experience. The most basic element of human movement relies solely on the nervous system. Muscles do not get the signal to "go" unless the nervous system directs them to do so!

THE NERVOUS SYSTEM AND MOVEMENT

The brain, spinal cord and nerves make up the basic elements of the nervous system. The nervous system represents the control tower for communication and directs movement for the entire body. In a basic sense, we move because information is received and forwarded via the nervous system and its specialized messengers, the sensory organs, to the skeletal muscles of the body. Quite simply, the brain controls muscular movement and "thinks" in terms of whole motions to attain a synchronized movement pattern (Jackson, 1931; Korr, 1976; reported in Wolf, 2001).

Understanding human movement becomes easier with a realization that "exercise is muscle contraction." More specifically, movement relates to "muscular force production" rather than "muscle contraction." Why? Because not all muscular force development refers to a tension building process of "contraction," which results in a shortening of the muscle and is referred to as a "concentric contraction." A muscle can also produce force where the length of the muscle does not change (isometric force production), where the "contraction" produces an increase in tension but does not cause significant movement at the joint, or where the muscle exerts tension while lengthening, which represents eccentric force production (Plowman and Smith, 1997).

Traditional approaches to conditioning, as well as functional types of training, incorporate concentric, eccentric and isometric types of force production. One type of training or force production is not superior to the other, but *all* are essential to a well-rounded program that meets *all* the requirements of a forward-looking program. In turn, a progressive and complete training program will meet *all* the requirements that contribute to proficient human movement.

NEURAL CONTROL OF HUMAN MOVEMENT

The study of neuromuscular control in human movement provides the science that backs, and helps us to understand how balance training works, and why it is important. As mentioned, *all* human movement, skilled or unskilled, is dependent on muscle contraction or force production, which in turn is one hundred percent dependent on receiving a signal from the nervous system. A muscle that is not activated by the nervous system is a muscle that does not contribute to movement. This fact implies that muscles must "learn" how to contribute to skilled movement patterns through training and repetition that is specific to the movement(s) being undertaken. Activity like this is usually referred

to as "skill practice," "sport specific training" or "rehearsal." The principle of skill-rehearsal encompasses specificity -- specific practice and repetition -- and is the most important fundamental aspect related to motor learning and high-level performance.

As a result of training in a specific manner, for given activities, the nervous system is able to call on and activate groups of muscle fibers (motor units) at the precise moment needed, as well as call into play the correct number of motor units to develop the "right" amount of force needed for the activity. As an example, removing an eyelash from the surface of the cornea requires a different amount of muscle force production when compared to slam-dunking a basketball or pressing a 1 RM (repetition maximum) amount of weight. An ability to mediate muscular force development is called "rate coding," or as referred to earlier, as a "gradation of response" (Plowman and Smith, 1997).

The ability to gradually and progressively control muscular force output, up or down, for a given movement, is obviously a critical aspect of successful and skilled human movement. The ability to regulate force development depends on the nervous system, with the other key aspect being tied to mechanical factors (i.e., length-tension-angle, force-velocity and elasticity-force relationships, as well as architectural design of the muscle) that influence muscle contraction in the body (Plowman and Smith, 1997). The type of regulatory control this discussion is most concerned with is neural and is, as previously mentioned, referred to as a "gradation of response" or "rate coding."

The body's capability to manage muscular force development is vital to productive and effective movement. Human performance – balance responses included – is directly dependent on the correct application of force. If you are going to launch a shot-put, slam a tennis serve, recover from a stumble, rise from a chair, stand upright, blink an eye or eat an ice cream cone, you must be able to apply the right amount of muscular force. (Can you imagine the result of eating an ice cream cone if you tried to lift it toward your face and could not regulate force production?)

MUSCLE FIBERS AND MOTOR UNITS

The physiologic reason behind your ability to regulate force production lies in the fact that movement is based on contractions of motor units (force production output), and not single muscle fibers, nor entire muscles. A number of muscle fibers make up a motor unit, and many motor units are contained within each muscle. The body's muscles are comprised of both fast and slow twitch muscle fibers. Each type of fiber has a different threshold at which they will fire or activate. Slow twitch muscles have a lower stimulus threshold so they will fire or be called into action sooner, and will continue to perform the work load until the activity demands a more powerful contraction, at which time the fast twitch motor units will be activated (Brooks, 2001; Brooks, 1997).

Motor units, of which there are many in each muscle, are made up of either all fast or slow twitch fibers. When a motor unit is activated, or in other words, the stimulus from the nervous system is great enough to cross its threshold, all of the muscle fibers associated with the motor unit will be called into action. This is known as the "all-or-none" principle of muscle contraction. Mistakenly, many people believe this means that a muscle fires all-or-none. It does not. If this were true and you tried to move the ice cream cone that was mentioned earlier in this text to your mouth, you would violently smash it into your face! What is true is that *motor units* and

their associated fibers *do* fire all-or-none. But, to reiterate, a muscle is comprised of many motor units, of which each is made up of *all* fast or slow twitch fibers. Each type of motor unit – fast or slow twitch – has a different threshold or point at which it will activate in response to neural stimuli.

These facts explain why you can command your body to perform gross, explosive physical movement in a skilled fashion, yet you can also remove a speck of dirt from your eye without ramming your finger into your eye socket. Real-life movement requires this complex and subtle interplay, which is developed through "practice." Practice can be thought of as a combination of goal oriented training and "specific play," as well as combining this with actual participation in the specific sport(s) or activity in which you are trying to improve.

If skill is going to improve to the next level in "your" sport, for example – downhill skiing – no matter how much you train balance and functional core strength, water ski, or inline skate to simulate the specificity of ski edge-control, at some point you have to transition the skill, strength, balance, agility or flexibility attained through these efforts to the specific sport. Simply, you have to glide downhill on snow! On the other hand, health and fitness gains can be thought of as nonspecific, and using various types of training is more than adequate for this type of goal to be accomplished, as long as all programming needs are addressed.

REFLEX CONTROL OF MOVEMENT

An intellectual discussion of coordinated movement must always include a reference to bodily reflexes, and the systems that govern motor-movement reflex feedback. These systems obviously play an important role. A reflex is a rapid, involuntary response that results in a specific motor response (Plowman and Smith, 1997), with that response being dependent on the type and duration of the stimulus received. Skilled movement depends a great deal upon your body's ability to respond to stimuli with an unconscious, or automatic, movement reaction.

Reflexes can be categorized into autonomic or somatic (soma refers to the body) categories. Autonomic reflexes activate cardiac and smooth muscle and glands, whereas somatic reflexes result in skeletal muscle contraction (Plowman and Smith, 1997). Somatic reflexes are, of course, most important to a discussion that focuses on movement.

The spinal cord serves as the crucial link between the brain and peripheral nervous system (i.e., nerves that serve the extremities or limbs). The spinal cord is involved in both voluntary and involuntary movements, and besides serving as the information conduit between the brain and peripheral nervous system, it is also the site at which reflex integration occurs (Plowman and Smith, 1997). In other words, information moves into and out of the spinal cord via spinal nerves that exit from each side and along the length of the cord. Information must be transmitted via the brain and the spinal nerves, and then must be *integrated* in a manner that results in useful or necessary movement. Along this information highway, data is carried up and down the spinal cord via a series of tracts, or bundles of fibers, in the central nervous system. Some tracts are responsible for transmitting sensory information (i.e., pressure, temperature, visual, sound, changes in equilibrium), whereas others carry motor, or movement information and regulate a continuum of movement that ranges from delicate or fine movement, to gross physical skills that require explosive and maximal force output.

THE ROLE OF MECHANORECEPTORS

Mechanoreceptors are specialized sensory cells which process a physical stimulus into a neurologic signal that can be interpreted by the central nervous system (CNS), with the end result giving you the ability to monitor and control joint position and movement. Mechanoreceptors have critical roles in not only providing feedback about joint position sense, but also in controlling muscle tone and impacting reflex response (Laskowski et al., 1997).

Each of four mechanoreceptor sites – currently thought to be key information receptors and to trigger dynamic joint stability – include cutaneous, joint capsule, muscle and ligamentous receptors. All are thought to contribute to joint position sense, and the muscle receptors which are found in the muscle spindle and Golgi tendon organ are important to both proprioception and motor control of the muscles (Laksowski et al., 1997). Mechanoreceptors can be stimulated by a variety of feedback or stimuli.

PROPRIOCEPTION, EQUILIBRIUM, BALANCE AND ASSOCIATED REFLEXES

Proprioception is a term that refers to the normal, ongoing awareness of body position or joint position sense. Automatic adaptations and responses to stimuli, that impact body position and state-of-balance, are ever-present and ongoing in the body. Sensory feedback, which tells you how your body or a body part is positioned, is regulated by proprioceptors or sensory organs. All senses are important. A host of sensory receptors that include the eyes, ears and specialized sensory receptors located in muscles, tendons and joints provide us with a constant barrage of information that keeps us appraised of bodily motion, position of body parts and how both interact to tell us if the body is responding efficiently as a whole. This feedback gives us the necessary information to make physical adjustments, if necessary.

Visual senses, or sight, give us immediate feedback about the speed or direction a ball or opponent may be moving, and is extremely important to skilled performance and balance. Try to stand on the BOSU dome with your eyes closed, and it quickly becomes apparent that visual stimulus is very important to balance. Hearing is important, too. The sound created by solid bat contact with a baseball gives information to fielders about the speed of the ball and even ground reaction conditions can be "felt" and "heard" (i.e., wet, spongy playing surface or an athlete's shoe sliding and losing contact with the playing surface), which gives the performer insight and feedback into what adjustments will be necessary as movement is continued. It is easy to conclude that movement is complex and influenced by a number of factors.

THE VESTIBULAR SYSTEM

The inner ear is equipped with specialized equilibrium receptors and is called the vestibular apparatus. Turn your head one way, then the other, or tip your ear toward one shoulder and you will experience how sensory receptors in the inner ear attempt to preserve equilibrium (balance) and maintain a steady head position. Fluid filled structures and specially arranged semicircular canals in the vestibular apparatus allow information about head movement, and speed of head movement, to be transmitted to the brain via an inner ear nerve (vestibulochoclear nerve). This information is processed in the brain along with any information being received from the visual receptors and the somatic receptors located in the muscles, tendons and joints (Plowman and Smith, 1997).

MUSCLE SPINDLES

Proprioceptive sense, and consequently balance, is available largely because of muscle spindles and other sensory organs or proprioceptive receptors. Sensory organs relay information via the central nervous system and provide you with a sense of body or limb position in space. This is also referred to as kinesthetic awareness. Sensory organs, located in muscles, tendons or joints, for example, allow a person to predict the degree of elbow flexion or extension even if the individual does not have the advantage of visual feedback. Therefore, balance training should include drills that both allow and discourage the use of sight, as this will challenge the somatic receptors of the body in different ways, which will challenge the body as whole, in a different manner.

The muscle spindle plays an important role in daily posture and has important implications for balance needs in general, for all movement. Muscle spindles are located in skeletal muscles, and lie parallel to and are imbedded in muscle fibers or muscle cells (Plowman and Smith, 1997, pg. 491). They are sensitive to the resting length of the muscle, changes in the length of the muscle and the speed at which lengthening occurs, and thus are stimulated by stretch. Information from the spindle is sent directly to the central nervous system via a reflex arc. This sensory feedback loop (the reflex arc) is made up of a sensory receptor (the muscle spindle and afferent neuron) and spinal nerve (efferent neuron). This reflex arc allows you to regularly adjust body position based on immediate physical demands, as presented by current stimuli, and to do so with little thought. Muscle spindles help the body maintain tone, posture, alignment and balance. Muscle spindles also provide a defense mechanism, through the stretch reflex (myotatic reflex), that can help prevent muscle injury. If the spindles perceive that a muscle is being stretched too quickly or stretched to an unsafe length, stimulation of the spindle would cause that muscle(s) to shorten reflexively. Examples of the myotatic reflex are exhibited by a patellar tendon tap, which results in a knee jerk response, or by the head jerk response that could occur if you were to fall asleep in a seated position.

Additionally, when muscle spindles are activated because of changes in the length of the muscle, (i.e. you are attempting to maintain balance over a changing or unstable surface) associated muscles will alternately contract and relax as a result of muscle spindle activation. This reaction, in turn, directly affects body position, balance and your center of gravity. You can see that the muscle spindle is involved in both sensory and motor functions. Challenging this automatic "correction factor" through functional balance practice and participation in a specific sport or activity, lays critical groundwork that leads to efficient, functional movement.

RECIPROCAL INNERVATION

This reflex inhibition involves agonist and antagonistic muscles. When a muscle group contracts, its opposing or antagonistic muscle group reflexively relaxes. Reflex relaxation of the antagonistic muscle occurs because of agonist contraction, and is tied to the muscle spindle. During general motor movement, reciprocal innervation is important because it allows for the occurrence of coordinated motor movement. During stretching, it is a reflex mechanism that can be taken advantage of to create a relaxed muscle. Potentially, invoking this response will allow for more effective stretching to take place because the muscle is relaxed when it, and associated fascia, is being stretched.

In summary, the muscle spindle is an important sensory feedback mechanism of the body. Not only does the spindle normally emit low-level sensory nerve signals that assist in maintaining muscle tone and affect constant postural adjustments throughout the day, feedback from the spindle also helps the muscles and body adjust movement requirements based on load or degree of effort required. Spindles influence skilled movement capabilities because of the spindle's dampening affect on skeletal muscles' agonist/antagonist relationship, which contributes to "smooth" movement (Plowman and Smith, 1997).

GOLGI TENDON ORGAN

The Golgi tendon organ (GTO) represents the last key sensory organ that impacts somatic reflexes. The GTOs are located within the tendonous attachment area of muscles and are stimulated by stretch or muscle contraction. GTOs transmit information about muscle tension, and if activated, cause associated muscle(s) to relax. This reflex inhibition of the muscle is called the inverse myotatic response.

This reflex action that results in a relaxed muscle is important to movement for several reasons. First, this reflex inhibition can be called into play when the GTOs "sense" that excessive tension in the muscle could cause the tendonous attachment(s) of the muscle to tear away, or rupture, from its bony attachment point. GTOs are responsible for a "muscle giving out" when under too much duress. As is true for muscle spindles and reciprocal inhibition, the GTO mediated response of muscular relaxation is useful for creating flexibility gains since muscle fibers that are relaxed do not get in the way of the stretching process, and are less likely to be strained or injured. Finally, sensory information gathered by the GTOs about tension development in the muscle allows for adjustments during movement that require only the needed tension, or force development, to successfully begin and finish movements with smooth transitions (Plowman and Smith, 1997).

AUTOMATIC INTEGRATION OF SENSORY SYSTEMS

This science section was introduced with a brief look at the complexities and skill involved in elite athletic participation. But, just as high-level sport performance represents a picture of extraordinary neuromuscular accomplishment, at even its simplest level, so does balance training and its maintenance. The key difference in perspective is that balance training is accessible to all, easy to do, fun and self-gratifying! Yet any skill level, as it relates to movement, is dependent on the intricate and precise participation of the central nervous system as it acts upon muscles, after receiving information. It is only through a complex, automatic integration of several sensory systems of the body, that we can accurately position our bodies, perceive where and how the body is positioned in space relative to our position, and easily adjust how much force we develop in our muscles to maintain precise performance boundaries, assure safe execution of the movement and maintain or recover alignment and center of gravity without a second thought.

The neuromuscular system's motor output – maintenance or recovery of body equilibrium – is directly influenced by the somatosensory, visual and vestibular systems. Training the various nervous and sensory receptor systems of the body with functional, balance and sport/activity specific training can lead to more efficient, accurate and highly skilled movement patterns. Skilled movement is more energy efficient, safer and it feels better. Moving gracefully and performing better are just two reasons why functional training is important to all who want to move efficiently and with purpose.

The importance of a broad-ranged plan of attack that includes functional, traditional and specific exercise/practice is apparent. A complete approach should:

1. Teach the nervous system how to regulate muscular force production.

2. Improve proprioception or awareness of your body's position, or any of its parts, and how they are positioned.

3. Develop more skillful and energy efficient movement patterns.

4. Train flexibility, cardiorespiratory endurance, stabilizing strength, muscular strength and endurance – and develop power, which combines an element of strength with speed of movement.

Functional training incorporates the concepts of balance/stability training and closed chain exercise (CCE) by requiring the body's natural motor reflexes to react as an integrated unit. In other words, the whole body is challenged to participate in order to maintain correct posture and balance while moving. The inclusion of activities that involve the entire body in a dynamic and coordinated fashion represents the development of functional fitness. This type of fitness is easily transferred to daily tasks, recreation and sport. Stabilization and functional training can both be integrated into closed chain and open chain exercise as explained in the following sections. But, remember that functional training ultimately trains movement, not just stabilizing contractions that contribute to effective movement. Stability and balance training represent two aspects of training that fit under the "functional training umbrella."

UNDERSTANDING CLOSED AND OPEN CHAIN EXERCISE

To best understand whether you are performing a closed chain exercise (CCE) or open chain exercise (OCE), it is useful to view your body as a length of chain. Envision your arms and legs as opposite ends of the chain.

Open chain exercise occurs when an end segment of the chain (arms or legs) is not fixed and does not support the weight of your body. An example of OCE is a seated knee extension or an arm curl.

Closed chain exercise occurs if either set of limbs (hands or feet) is involved in supporting the weight of your body. A squat or lunge movement is a good illustration of CCE. The legs and feet bear the weight of your body. CCE requires a dynamic response from the whole body to perform the movement correctly, safely and most efficiently.

Though not classically defined as CCE, any exercise that partially supports your body weight and requires an integrated response from the body's musculature can be characterized as CCE. A push-up position that is held with your feet placed on the dome of the BOSU is a good example. Your arms and hands partially bear the weight of your body and an end segment of the chain (your hands) is "closed," "fixed" or weight bearing.

Many experts believe that effective rehabilitation and strengthening exercise is *not* best developed by stabilizing one part of the body in a non-weight bearing position, and then isolating another body part, as is exemplified by the seated leg extension and OCE. While there are certainly many proper applications of OCE, this traditional approach may not stimulate the body to react in a natural way. OCE is best characterized by isolation, whereas CCE is best referred to as

dynamic, functional, and working in concert with the body as a whole, integrated unit. Both types of training, depending on application and participant needs, are considered excellent ways to condition the body. The best results will be realized when you use both approaches.

Natural and functional movement is directly related to the harmonious workings of joints, muscles and the neurological system. Our neurological systems interact with our musculoskeletal system in a coordinated and complex manner. Using stability or balance training, and CCE, is the perfect way to stimulate and train this complex interaction of the body. After all, this is the way we normally function every moment of our lives. Think about common activities and you'll realize that most movements are dependent on coordinated balance and changing force output throughout the body.

Demands placed on the body during stability training, balance training and closed chain exercise vary dramatically, but replicate daily life and sport situations. From moment to moment, the body strives to maintain balance and to integrate the responses into safe, skilled movement. This mirrors daily activities where our bodies constantly perform in many planes of movement. Because of this, we need to challenge our bodies on a regular basis with these types of movement training.

TEN CHARACTERISTICS OF FUNCTIONAL TRAINING

· · · · ·

For activity or training to be considered functional it should:

1. *FOCUS ON INTEGRATED MOVEMENT, NOT ISOLATED ACTION AT A JOINT.* You must practice parts of the movement, combine the parts into movement patterns, practice the movement, rehearse the movement, "drill" the movement and "do" the activity or sport. Functional movement integrates multiple joint movements – linking movement together in the kinetic chain – and doesn't isolate muscles, but instead requires significant stabilization of the body's musculature during dynamic movement.

2. *PRESENT AN UNPREDICTABLE MOVEMENT CHALLENGE.* Sport participation, by its nature, represents imbalance, and an uncontrolled, dynamic environment. All movement exhibits a degree of randomness and chaos. On the other hand, some elements of "play" are fixed. For example, a diver or gymnast contends with fixed challenges that are presented by height of a diving board, spring of a vaulting board or the challenge of quieting the movement of still rings. A tennis player or downhill ski racer interact with fixed elements that include using a familiar racquet with a specific string tension, or skiing a familiar race course on a favorite pair of well-tuned skis. But, athletes also contend with changing elements that can include wind, snow conditions, terrain uncertainties or in the case of a tennis player, an opponent who counters with unpredictable strategies, of which all can impact performance. Some coaches contend that what separates anarchy from sport is a thinly veiled line that represents uncontrolled chaos versus controlled chaos as it relates to movement.

Functional movement is dynamic and requires the participant to speed up, slow down, stop, change directions, react to ground forces, contend with gravitational forces, alter the amount of force production, stabilize, change body angles, modify line of sight and constantly adjust, readjust and react.

3. *INTRODUCE MULTI-JOINT MOVEMENT THAT OCCURS IN MULTIPLE PLANES OF MOVEMENT.* Your body, the live representation of the kinetic chain principle, moves in multi-planar fashion whether you're performing at a world-class level or lifting your child. Functional movement occurs in a three-dimensional environment at any level of physical movement and challenges multi-planar movement. To challenge movement functionally, you must exercise in the sagital plane (divides the body into right and left halves as it passes front-to-back), frontal plane (divides the body into front and back halves as it passes side-to-side) and transverse plane (divides the body into top and bottom halves). Within these basic planes of movement are infinite movement variation possibilities. In other words, you must bend, reach, stretch and maintain balance simultaneously while creating force production via the kinetic chain.

4. *BUILD COMPLEXITY IN A PROGRESSIVE MANNER.* Foundational fitness must be attained and basic movement skills learned before advanced training and balance skills are attempted. This will ensure success, safety and progressive skill advancement.

5. *BUILD INTENSITY IN A PROGRESSIVE MANNER.* Baseline strength, muscular endurance and cardiorespiratory fitness must first be established. Initial loading during functional training should be accomplished by using body weight only. If appropriate, progress to external resistance as training adaptations take place and specificity of training dictates. Many people hurt themselves or their performance in the name of "specificity." For example, it is arguable that excessively "loading" a golf swing or baseball pitcher's arm motion while the skill is performed at full speed is dangerous, not specific and could negatively affect the complex neuromuscular patterns involved in complex sport movements. (Refer to number 8 for additional information.)

6. **DEVELOP THE BODY'S ABILITY TO STABILIZE AND GENERATE POWER FROM THE CORE OR TRUNK "POWER CENTER."** A variety of movements and types of training must be used to ensure a balanced approach to core training, as well as total development of the trunk region. Core movements should be trained in isolation (mover-type activity that includes spinal flexion, extension, lateral flexion and rotation), as well as using functional exercises that require the trunk muscles to synchronize their activation, resulting in a stabilized pelvic and spinal position. Functional or stabilization training of the abdominal region represents synergistic movement that demands an integrated, interdependent response of the trunk—which means muscles working together to stabilize spinal position. Functional training of the abdominal and back muscles involves training them in a manner in which they are required to work on a daily basis. The key function of the abdominal and back musculature is not to create movement at the spine, but to exert isometric or stabilizing muscular force production in order to maintain spinal and pelvic position. (Note: These comments are not intended to infer that mover-

type or isolation trunk exercises are poor choices. The intention is to recognize that stabilization training is different than active-isolation exercise, which utilizes movement at the spine, and that both should be used to optimally develop and challenge the trunk.)

7. **CHALLENGE JOINT MOTIONS IN A MANNER THAT CLOSELY COPIES WHAT THE BODY IS REQUIRED TO DO IN THE ACTIVITY IN WHICH YOU WILL PARTICIPATE.** The adage, "Train and practice like you play!" is a testament to kinetic chain or functional training, and the importance of specificity.

8. **"DRILL" OR PRACTICE IN A MANNER THAT INCORPORATES SKILLS THAT ARE INTEGRAL TO THE PERFORMANCE OF AN ACTIVITY OR SPORT.** Using drills for the sake of drills is unintentional training. Analyze the activity and incorporate movement and balance challenges that mirror the activity, but do not introduce unnecessary risk.

9. **HAVE A SPECIFIC APPLICATION IN MIND FOR ACCOMPLISHING YOUR TRAINING GOALS.** Activity for the sake of activity is a dead end approach that goes nowhere. Without specific training goals, you or your participants will drop out, become discouraged or get less than optimal training/performance result. Training must make sense and have application toward what you are trying to accomplish if it is to be called functional or useable training.

10. **BE FUN.** Functional training, by its very nature is fun. Though it can be challenging, it is generally rewarding and synchs-up with how you move naturally. Since it feels natural and is challenging, yet has direct links to personal success and every day movement applications, "fun" takes care of itself in the form of diversity, results and exercise compliance.

PLACING FUNCTIONAL TRAINING
IN PROPER PERSPECTIVE

• • • • •

Functional training can simply be referred to as a process that "trains, or develops, movement coordination." Hopefully, every professional can identify with the simplicity, yet profound nature of this characterization, as well as its importance to skilled and safe movement.

Secondly, functional training and its principles emphasize the fact that fitness programs cannot remain one-dimensional. Effective programming must employ a variety of science-backed methodologies that cover all health, fitness and performance bases. Too much of a "good thing," or more specifically "one thing," signifies a rut. What science *can* say for certain is that *no* single approach creates a comprehensive training plan that optimizes health, fitness and/or performance.

Industry discussion and controversy about what constitutes functional training, as well as the merits of so-called nonfunctional training, highlights the importance of placing all types of training, including functional approaches, in proper perspective (ACE Certified News, Vol. 7, No. 6, Oct./Nov., 2001). Granted, an important training goal for any program would involve improvement of functional movement capabilities, or training the body to move as a whole, in a world that doesn't rely greatly on movement isolation. To accomplish this goal a program must include movement training which is dependent on neuromuscular integration and movement coordination. But, does this acknowledgement imply that development of strength and hypertrophy in traditional, isolation or nonfunctional approaches cannot contribute to function and neuromuscular integration? An accurate and science based response would say "No!"

The "functional camp" might argue that the nervous system and its command center, the brain, do not "know" or recognize individual muscles. However, this is a simplified and weak argument that would support a view that training muscles for strength, or in isolation, can contribute nothing or little to functional, integrated movement. Certainly, the brain and nervous system do "know" individual muscles. It is by training movement specificity – functional training – that you can transition non-specific strength development of individual muscles into muscular force production and force output that has the capacity to move the skeletal framework in a manner that is consistent with skilled movement. In other words, this type of approach exemplifies functional or activity specific training and incorporates the idea of "transitioning" non-specific training adaptations and skills.

Activity that can do this, for example, requires you to balance over your center of gravity, and use neural reflexes, closed chain movement, strength, endurance, power, flexibility, balance, coordination and agility. All of these bodily systems and movement related attributes must be challenged and developed in an integrated manner if the goal is coordinated movement and complete development. This acknowledgement related to transitioning non-specific adaptations does *not* constitute support for a conclusion that states, "other types of training are irrelevant to functional movement."

Developing strength before, or concurrently with functional-type exercise, *can* contribute to improved system and/or bodily function. Take the argument for increasing strength and size (hypertrophy) of muscles for runners with a nonfunctional approach, as an example. Runners who only run will lose bone, muscle mass and strength. Muscle mass and strength cannot be maintained or developed to any great degree with running alone. From an elite performance perspective, runners don't want excessive muscle mass, but strength maintenance is important for injury prevention and posture maintenance. From a health/fitness perspective, strength maintenance is more important, but the key issue is that high levels of strength cannot be maintained by running lots of miles or using running specific drills. At some phase in a comprehensive training program, everyone can benefit from a traditional strength training program.

From a broader programming perspective, strong muscles can produce higher forces and can exhibit more endurance at submaximal levels of effort, when compared to weak muscles. Strong muscles can produce higher levels of, and sustain force production, which will aid the body in "learning" movements, as well as helping to maintain consistent and high-levels of performance. Strength provides the foundation for muscular endurance, agility, coordination and balance.

Regardless of how strength is gained, it can contribute to skilled movement and improve sport performance. A good example of this non-specific carry over is exemplified in the sport of golf. The golf swing is a very athletic, skill-based and complex biomechanical process. Putting calls for a great degree of eye-hand coordination, while driving requires a high level of effort and power. The drive, which is ballistic and power oriented, can be performed more effectively, safely and forcefully by developing physical conditioning which complements these requirements. It is challenging, to say the least, to develop golf-swing specific exercises that would develop this aspect of the game. In fact, trying to duplicate the

golf swing with added external resistance is probably detrimental to skill/neuromuscular development, and could increase the participant's risk of injury. The best practice for improving the golf swing is accomplished under the skilled direction of a professional, on the golf course. But, club head speed and driving distance, for example, can be increased with a non-specific strength and flexibility program. Additionally, injury potential can be reduced in the shoulder and back, as well as the hips, elbows and wrists by learning correct golf swing mechanics and by engaging in consistent and appropriate strength, flexibility and cardiovascular conditioning programs (Westcott, 1997; Westcott, et al., 1996).

Smart and effective training progressions for any fitness goal(s) should include the development of flexibility, stabilizing strength, muscular strength, power, activity specific movement drills and exercises, and a lot of time spent participating in the actual activity(s) or sport of choice. Many athletes and fitness enthusiasts have been injured when power – or ballistic-type training – even so called sport-specific training – is placed before important foundational training elements, or otherwise introduced prematurely.

This backbone of a training program should be developed by establishing a base of balanced strength, cardiovascular and flexibility conditioning before training higher-risk power or agility, for example. Stretching, functional stabilizing strength and development of "traditional" strength (placing the body under load, i.e., 6-20 repetitions) can help you maintain balance or skill. In other words, a *complete* approach to training sets the stage whereby you can set yourself up for a successful experience with functional training.

The bottom line is that movement is dependent, in part, on strength. It's harder to exhibit good balance throughout the day or demonstrate skilled movement if you don't possess adequate muscular strength and endurance, or sufficient cardiorespiratory endurance. There must be no weak links in your chain of biological systems that are dependent upon one another for optimal body function. This holds true from both a health/fitness, and movement in general or performance perspective. That is why it is equally inappropriate to turn away from isolated strength training, or to balk at the idea of incorporating functional training concepts into your program. Program design that excludes proven and important methods of training will result in a limited approach to fitness and a program that is far from optimal for participants.

All aspects of fitness influence function and functional movement. These systems do not exist in isolation and include both isolated and integrated movement patterns related to cardiorespiratory, muscular strength and endurance and flexibility training. Instead, they are dependent upon one another for creating optimal performance and biological function in the human body. By nature, the human body is integrated, interdependent and linked via its numerous systems.

WHAT AFFECTS BALANCE?

• • • • •

Regardless of how you challenge balance or train functional movement, muscle spindles and other motor reflexes will be involved in the process as they constantly route stimuli via the central nervous system to the muscles, thus providing critical information about body position. When discussing function or balance, it must be placed in the context of neuromuscular reflexes and take place in a world where gravitational forces constantly influence movement.

GRAVITY, GROUND REACTION FORCES AND MOMENTUM

If you are to move efficiently against gravity while on your feet, you must possess adequate range of motion, joint mobility, muscle strength and muscle endurance, as well as have the ability to coordinate movement, align the body and react when weight or a body part is shifted into a variety of planes. Reacting – pushing, rotating or pivoting off stable ground or an impressionable, unstable surface like the BOSU dome – is the foundation of force development that contributes to movement, and ultimately power since power is a function of strength and speed of movement. It is important to reemphasize that power, speed, agility, function and balance are not independent of strength. However, it could be argued that balance, stabilizing strength and flexibility development should precede any other performance aspect of training.

Skilled movement, for most activities, ties directly into how ground reaction forces, between the foot and surface you're on, are corralled and transferred to intentional movement. The constant interplay that loads the muscles so you can generate power results from the continual playback

loop of 1) overcoming or neutralizing the force of gravity, 2) harnessing ground reaction forces and directing them, for example, to propel the body or twist the torso and 3) using momentum that is generated in steps one and two, to overcome inertia in an energy efficient way so that the body remains in motion. This interplay *is* functional movement and highlights the difference between training muscles in isolation versus training motion.

RIGHTING, PROTECTIVE AND EQUILIBRIUM REACTIONS

The antigravity, balance and power producing capacity of the body can be simply thought of, in terms of physical skills, as righting, protective and equilibrium reactions.

Automatic *righting reactions* maintain or restore body alignment as it relates to the position of the head, trunk and limbs. Muscle spindles monitor the rate at which muscles lengthen and play a big role in maintaining balance at rest. Spindle feedback helps you stay centered while standing on the dome and visually tracking your hand from in front of the body to the side, and then to an overhead position. Muscle spindles also play a role when you try to maintain balance over the center of the dome with your eyes closed. When a body part is suddenly displaced, righting reactions come into play. An arm or leg shooting up or out to the side counters the weight displacement and is largely automatic, thanks to sensory feedback coming from the muscle spindles. If weight shifts are slow and controlled, constant muscular activity and adjustment is subtle, rather than dramatic.

Protective reactions can also utilize the muscle spindles to prevent over-stretching of the muscle, or falling.

Equilibrium reactions can be thought of as an integration of *righting* and *protective reactions* as the body fine tunes, through practice, a coordinated, complex and automatic response. The aim of the response is to preserve or restore balance during any type of activity. Reactions and attempts to maintain balance are common whenever the center of gravity of the body is displaced over any base of support. When centered on the air-filled dome, this displacement is ever present as the properties of the dome provides a gel-like surface that continually attempts to displace the body's center of gravity.

HOW TO CHALLENGE PROPRIOCEPTION & BALANCE

Strategies for balance training focus on increasing sensory input, which ultimately improves motor skills, kinesthetic awareness and balance. At its core, functional training methods literally flood the neuromuscular system (brain, nerves and muscles) and create "smart muscles," in a neurological sense. "Smart muscles," versus "dumb muscles," influence movement in such a way as to make life activities and sports easier to perform. "Dumb muscles" can be transitioned to "smart muscles" with activity-specific neurological or functional movement training. Stated simply, you should eventually train – during moments of specific-play and practice – the body in a manner that replicates the activity or sport requirements in which you will participate. Because of this training, the central nervous system will store an internal blueprint of newly learned sensations that will help you to move more efficiently and safely. Training like this teaches the body to "remember" learned responses to imbalance, which limits inefficient and unnecessary movement.

THE BOSU BALANCE TRAINER EXPERIENCE

Working with the BOSU Balance Trainer creates a movement continuum from simple to most challenging, from static to dynamic, and from subtle balance adjustments to dramatic or highly-reactive responses. This aspect of BOSU training ensures immediate success for the most novice or deconditioned trainee. However, a new and progressive challenge is always waiting around the corner. This diversity is one reason why this type of functional and balance training is used by world-class athletes and their conditioning coaches world-wide. Yet, regardless of training

goal, this foundation of balance development and body awareness is important, and can be attained by everyone!

When working out on the BOSU Balance Trainer, you immediately realize that body or spatial awareness will be constantly challenged and that a variety of stimuli influence a balanced position. Whether you are holding a static balance, performing a dynamic balance movement, reaching up, across or behind you, twisting, jumping, spinning or "sticking" a landing on top of the BOSU dome, visual, auditory, inner ear and proprioceptive feedback will constantly alter and affect your performance.

Visual tracking drills (line of sight changes) can be used to challenge balance, as can elimination of feedback sources. For example, stand with both feet on the BOSU dome with your eyes open. Once you're centered, close your eyes. Note how difficult it is to remain centered on the dome and you'll feel the increased muscular challenge in the lower body, especially at the ankle. Balance and function can be challenged in a variety of positions on the BOSU that not only focus on standing positions, but include seated, supine, sidelying, kneeling and prone exercises. This type of training requires constant adjustment and attention from the participant. Both the mind and body must be engaged at all times.

When training on BOSU it is natural – because of the dynamic characteristics of the dome surface, demands of an exercise or because of imperfect skills – that you will regularly move into and out of balanced positions. This same fact holds true for real-life movement, which is why functional balance training is so important to daily life and sport requirements.

As discussed, many factors influence balance and skill that are related to proprioception. When stabilization and balance are required, as is true for most movement, perfection – staying perfectly symmetrical, upright and/or in balance – is *not* always possible or desirable. It is easier and appropriate to set stabilization and maintain it during a strength exercise performed with dumb-bells (i.e., retract the scapulae during a supine pressing movement and maintain neutral lumbar posture) when compared to a complex and dynamic sport skill, such as "setting up" to kick a soccer ball while running. By definition, this stabilization aspect of movement is complex, dynamic, ever changing and rarely static for long, though the goal is often to remain in balance, as well as to stabilize and control movement! It is no wonder that skilled, efficient, consistent and safe movement standards can be so elusive.

Therefore, it is apparent that training programs must move beyond only improving the "big three" of fitness, which are commonly cited as cardiovascular, strength and flexibility fitness. Body awareness, balance and muscular endurance, as they relate to posture and proper body alignment, must be developed because they are integral aspects of daily life, recreation, sport and play. Balance training on the BOSU allows you to train the "big three," while simultaneously integrating functional balance challenges that carry over into real-life and sport applications.

FUNCTIONAL PROGRAM DESIGN: TRAINING FOR MOVEMENT

Sport conditioning regimens for professional and elite athletes, and functional training programs for fitness enthusiasts should include a balanced approach that covers all aspects of conditioning and utilize the concept of periodization.

Establish a balanced approach by creating a base of strength, cardiovascular and flexibility conditioning before training power, anaerobic-type endurance and agility, for example. Though various skills and components of fitness can be trained simultaneously, if you have a basic fitness foundation you're more likely to find the road to optimizing success and less likely to incur injury along the training journey.

Periodization can simply be defined as "planned results." Periodization manipulates volume of work (reps, sets, minutes, frequency, type of training) and intensity of effort over specific time periods. Periodization principles and science emphatically underline the importance of varying a training approach with a pre-thought-out through-line. It also underscores the idea that training one way, all of the time, is the wrong way, or at the least, is not the best possible way to train if optimization of training result is one of your goals. A critical component of a well thought-out periodized program includes the placement of rest, maintenance and recovery phases in the overall plan.

To complement traditional strength development (i.e., in the "weight room") and to help transition non-specific strength or fitness gains of any kind, it is important to include sport-specific drills. Drills that fall into this category, along with functional training activities, will prepare those you train for the varied demands of a wide variety of sports and activities.

CONDITIONING FOR MOVEMENT

Following are physical capabilities that are important to most individuals who regularly participate in sport, recreation or any type of formal training program.

STRENGTH

Strength provides the foundation for muscular endurance, speed, agility, balance, coordination and flexibility (you can't *actively* stretch an antagonist muscle without a strong agonist muscle). Mistakenly, many people believe strength development is somehow separate from these important athletic qualities. But, the truth is that strength is an attribute that is indispensable to all, and cannot be developed to any great degree without progressive overload (Brooks 1997; Brooks 2001).

On the other hand, it is true that raw strength developed by isolated movement for the sake of muscle hypertrophy or vanity, will not translate to functional movement by itself, to any significant degree. Strength that is gained in traditional training approachs can be easily transitioned to more usable or functional strength with practice and specific training. Developing high levels of strength, training functional movement patterns and practicing the specific activity you are going to participate in regularly, just might be the magic training formula for high-level performance in sports that require balance, power, agility and coordination. Developing balanced strength throughout the body can help maintain and develop balance, skill and performance!

POWER

The ability to use strength quickly (although not necessarily maximal strength) is very important to, for example, successfully slide downhill on snow or to perform Olympic-type lifts. Suddenly correcting and regaining balance or quickly changing direction are good examples of how strength is used, in the form of power, in many sports (i.e., skiing, snowboarding, inline skating, soccer, gymnastics, diving, hiking on uneven terrain, etc.) and daily activities (i.e., following a toddler, yard work, taking groceries out of a car, etc.). Competitive Olympic and power lifting focuses on the production of maximal force, strength and power. The training goal is 1 RM lifting, or lifting the most amount of weight that can be accomplished during two (Olympic) or three (power lifting) competitive lifts.

Most traditional strength training equipment allows you to strength train the muscle with a speed variable, but probably doesn't allow for specificity of training. For training to be specific, it must exactly replicate the neuromuscular or motor patterns of the activity. Close, in terms of specificity, is *not* specific! The exact timing, correct amount of force or strength, and speed of movement are the key issues that must be the same if it is going to be accurately claimed that a movement or type of training is truly specific in nature. But, any training adaptation or fitness gain *can* be transitioned to skill or performance that *is* specific.

ENDURANCE

How should endurance be defined? A marathon runner or Ironman triathlete requires endurance, as does a wrestler, downhill ski racer, and gymnast, not to mention competitors in the World's Strongest Man Competition. Yet, a competitive marathon runner or Ironman triathlete requires endurance over a period of hours, whereas a ski racer, wrestler, gymnast or "strongest man" competitor may have to endure, or produce muscular force, for "only" several seconds to a few minutes.

Cardiorespiratory or steady-rate endurance is different than sports oriented muscular endurance where moderate- to high-levels of force must be sustained for relatively short periods of time. Steady-rate cardiorespiratory training and endurance represents an activity like cycling, running, walking, swimming or stepping on and off the BOSU for periods of about 3-minutes or more. This type of low-level force production can be sustained for many minutes by a reasonably conditioned person. It's commonly referred to as cardiovascular conditioning.

On the other hand, muscular endurance can be referred to in a "local" manner, versus systemic. Systemic refers to the heart, vascular system and muscles and their ability to deliver and use oxygen, and thus sustain low-level force production over longer periods of time. The ability to sustain muscular endurance or the ability to endure repeated contractions at a moderate to high-level of force production from a few seconds to about a couple of minutes, could be characterized as being able to do so at a "local" level – meaning within a specific muscle or group of muscles. This type of "local" fatigue, which occurs within a few seconds to several minutes and is often associated with a burning sensation in related muscles due to lactic acid accumulation, is generally a result of anaerobic energy production. The higher level of lactic acid production is tied to the higher level of force production required, as the body is not able to produce the necessary force and energy production within aerobic pathways and must rely on anaerobic energy production with its resultant byproduct, and accumulation, of lactic acid. Conversely, cardiorespiratory endurance is associated with *little* accumulation of lactic acid and the related activity can be kept up for relatively long periods of time.

Cardiorespiratory endurance training is the foundation for anaerobic effort and quick recovery from high-force output requirements, because ultimately, all movement, even recovery from anaerobic effort, requires oxidation. Oxidation represents the delivery and use of oxygen to aid the recovery process and reformation of energy bonds broken apart to reform ATP and CP, which in a sense are the energy currencies (useable forms of energy) of the body (Brooks, 1997, Plowman and Smith, 1997). Improved oxidative capacity which is represented by VO2 – the ability to efficiently deliver (heart rate x stroke volume) and use oxygen (a-VO2 difference) – enhances recovery from hard effort.

AGILITY

An accurate characterization of agility is the ability to rapidly change position and direction with no loss of performance. Agility enables a skier, snowboarder, hiker, athlete or other physically active person to maintain balance, fluidity of movement and safe performance even when an obstacle or environmental condition, such as a person, tree, rock, terrain change or gust of wind, makes a quick reaction, adjustment or recovery necessary. Agility can be fully developed only when you have a base of strength, power and endurance. Power and agility performance decrease when endurance decreases. Simply, when you get tired, skill level deteriorates. Can you maintain high levels of performance and reaction even when your muscles are burning and you're at a breaking point? If you can't, it might represent the difference between winning or avoiding injury.

BALANCE AND COORDINATION

Kinesthetic awareness and control of the ankle, along with stabilization of the trunk, are especially important for keeping the center of gravity over your feet. If you're a skier or snowboarder, for example, the best place to learn balance for your sport occurs when you're on snow. In-line skating (add ski poles with rubber tips for skiers) and skate boarding (don't forget all-terrain skate or long boards, too) for snowboarders are other good examples of sport specific, no-snow training options. Additionally, static and dynamic balance exercises/drills on the unstable BOSU dome are other excellent choices.

FLEXIBILITY

A comprehensive and balanced flexibility program targets all of the major muscle groups of the body. Areas to focus on should include the backs of the lower legs and Achilles tendon area, quadriceps, hip flexors, hamstrings and gluteus maximus, as well as the fronts of the shoulder and chest. It is also important to develop trunk and pelvic mobility.

PROPRIOCEPTION TRAINING & ITS APPLICATION TO REHABILITATION

Proprioception training – the sense of body and joint position – is equally important from an injury prevention or rehabilitation perspective. Restoring (rehabilitating) or maintaining (prevention) proprioception allows the body to maintain stability and body orientation during static and dynamic activities. Injury or loss of fitness can interrupt your ability to sense body position.

PROPRIOCEPTION IN REHABILITATION AND INJURY PREVENTION PROGRAMS

During rehabilitation, proprioceptive programs are specifically tailored to each patient, and as is true for any functional program, should include balance training, closed kinetic chain exercise (CCE) like leg presses, single leg hops or jumps, back strengthening exercise and quadruped stabilization (i.e., positioned on the hands and knees or "all-fours" to stabilize the scapulae in a closed-kinetic chain position), as well as sport specific training and drills (Laskowski et al., 1997).

It is believed that impaired "joint position sense," when overlooked in a rehabilitation program, may be a leading cause for recurrent injuries. On the other hand, proprioceptive and balance training have been shown to significantly reduce the incidence of anterior cruciate ligament (ACL) injury in soccer players (reported in Laskowski et al., 1997, pg. 97). The goal of proprioceptive training during rehabilitation is to maximize protection from injury and restore one hundred percent, or optimal, function (Laskowski, et al., 1997). From this perspective, it would make perfect sense that this type of functional and balance training would be a necessary part of *any* training or rehabilitation program, and be appropriate for all types of people, regardless of program goals.

Rehabilitation and injury prevention oriented programs can be designed to challenge, enhance and improve the proprioceptive system. By affecting (training) various central nervous system pathways and reflex arcs, "prophylactic" (protective) proprioception training programs may protect against injury (Caraffa et al., reported in Laskowski et al., 1997).

STATIC AND DYNAMIC JOINT STABILITY

A major category of proprioceptive or functional training is balance training. An example of training the proprioceptive system and joint stability in a mostly *static* way includes one-legged standing balance exercises. The ability of appropriately activated muscles to stabilize a joint during more complex movement defines *dynamic* joint stability (Laskowski, 1997, pg. 98). Progressive and dynamic challenges, for example, hopping from one BOSU to another on one leg, jumping vertically and landing on the dome or performing pushups on the platform side of the BOSU while simultaneously keeping the platform level, changes the nature of the required joint stability to "dynamic."

CLOSED KINETIC CHAIN MOVEMENT AND JOINT STABILITY

Kinetic chain exercises tie closely into understanding whether static or dynamic joint stability is required or being trained. Another way to view closed kinetic chain (CCE) exercises is to view them as a type of movement in which movement at one joint produces predictable movement at other joints (Laskowski et al., 1997). Kinetic movement – the linking of movement from joint to joint while maintaining necessary joint stabilization – challenges the dynamic and reflexive aspects of proprioception in the legs and feet, and closely replicates the closed chain manner in which the lower extremities function in daily life and sport. Examples of kinetic closed chain (CCE) movements that can be challenged and integrated with balance challenges on the BOSU, include leg press, lunge or squatting motion, running, bounding or leaping forward or laterally, single leg hops, double leg hops, single and double leg vertical jumps, jump tucks, long jumps and cross-over running (carioca) or walking, to name a few. Whether from a health/fitness/sport performance, injury prevention or rehabilitation perspective, it is apparent that physical programs oriented toward healing, performance or efficient and safe movement should include activity that challenges both static and dynamic joint stability.

Upper Body Closed Chain Exercise

The upper extremities, which include the wrists, shoulders and scapulothoracic joints can also be challenged in closed chain fashion by bearing weight on the hands, which provides proprioceptive feedback to the arm, shoulder and scapular muscles. This type of multidirectional force exerts a rapid and varied change in direction of the applied force, largely because of balance challenges and bodily shifts that occur when performing a variety of exercises. For example, excellent joint stability exercises for the upper body include exercise performed in a quadruped position (i.e., positioned on "all fours") on the BOSU or even a firm surface, prone positions when doing a pushup from the knees or feet and when a straight body prone plank-position is held. Positions like these can stimulate functional scapulothoracic and glenohumeral (arm and shoulder) movement. Additionally, manual resistance that is applied quickly in several directions is considered "proprioceptively enriched" (Laskowski et al., 1997) and provides the benefits of closed chain exercise, as does resistance training (i.e., using cables or dumbbells which present a balance/stabilizing challenge) where significant balance and stabilization is required to perform the strength movement.

Proprioception And Stability Training For Low-Back Pain

Proprioceptive, lumbar stabilization training has become an increasingly popular method of training for the low-back muscles (Laskowski et al., 1997). This type of training involves "coordinated" training of all of the trunk muscles and its importance indicates that the abdominal and back muscles work together in not only preventing low-back pain, but in all skilled movement. The trunk or "power center" is often the weak link in the kinetic movement chain, and can inhibit the smooth and efficient transfer of movement power from upper to lower body, or vice-versa. In standing, prone, supine or side-lying positions, stabilization training focuses on establishing a neutral pelvic or lumbar posture, maintaining good skeletal alignment and developing strength and flexibility equally between all trunk muscles. Functional training not only develops stabilizing strength, but can also include training for "mover" or isolated strength.

However, current research (McGill, 2001; Kravitz, 2001) points to a defect in the body's motor control system, which controls joint stability through muscle co-activation. An inability to stabilize the spinal joints can lead to "buckling" because of fatigue that results from strenuous tasks or accumulated stress/fatigue of mundane daily tasks. Any kind of lapse – "buckling" or "collapse" of the spine – even a momentary one, can cause compression or rotation of the vertebrae which can lead to tissue irritation or injury. Spinal "buckling" can be minimized if the spinal musculature is strong enough to keep the spine positioned, or "stiff." McGill's research suggests that the correct balance of mobility and stabilizing strength may be the key to a healthy spine. Exercises that require co-activation of all of the spinal muscles – including the deep spinal rotators and stabilizers, and transversus muscle – can help to develop spinal stabilizing strength.

From a healthy back perspective, McGill believes training the trunk should focus on muscular endurance, rather than strength. It should be noted that elite level athletic participation can require more forceful production from the abdominal muscles, but generally, the function of the trunk muscles requires that they have sufficient endurance to stabilize spinal position during movement and throughout the day. He also believes the spine should be placed in a neutral position when loading it. This type of positioning reflects functional, stabilization training for the trunk and avoids extreme end-range of motion spinal flexion or extension. Note that this does not support the idea that the spine should *never* be fully flexed or extended. The focus of this type of training is on "bracing," which refers to a neuro-physiological event that requires the co-contraction of the deep spinal muscles, including the abdominal wall. Be wary of fixed leg sit ups, where the feet are anchored, as increased hip flexor activity and the reversal of the typical pull of the psoas muscle's insertion toward origin, is reversed, which results in increased compressive and shear loads in the low back. Even leg raises can cause spinal disc compression, especially if neutral lumbar posture is not maintained. Finally, McGill states that there is no single exercise that effectively challenges *all* of the trunk musculature. McGill indicates that a variety of isolation, or "mover-type," and stabilization exercises are needed to effectively and completely train the trunk.

PROPRIOCEPTION AND STABILITY TRAINING IN THE KNEE

Much of the research related to proprioception has focused on dynamic joint stability in the knee and attempted to assess what factors can alter strains imposed on the knee. Even ligaments, which are often thought of as innate mechanical restraints that stabilize joints, may supply the central nervous system with input that affects neuromuscular control of the knee (Palmer, I., reported in Laskowski, 1997). Though there is no precise model of how dynamic joint control is fully developed, the search is on, especially in light of recent increases in anterior cruciate ligament (ACL) injuries.

The chance of injury to the ACL in women is two to eight times greater when compared to men who train in the same sports, with similar rules and equipment (Arendt and Dick, 1995, American Journal of Sports Medicine, 23 (6), pps. 694-701). Two of the most common theories include anatomical differences between men and women, and female hormonal fluctuations/influences. Currently, the lack of sufficient and consistent research precludes any definitive conclusions about important gender differences that include anatomical and hormonal theories (Smith, 2001).

However, the role of movement patterns and how men or women are, and are *not*, being trained is quickly taking center stage on the scientific front. Proper preparation via intelligent training may be the prophylactic approach that is needed to minimize risk of injury at the knee. Specifically, scientific research is increasingly focusing on proprioception and neuromuscular control, and its affect on joint stability. One study (Griffin, 2000, Journal of the American Academy of Orthopaedic Surgeons, reported in Smith, 2001) concluded that, "Gender differences have been found in motion patterns, positions and forces generated from the hip and trunk to the knee." In an important investigative research project – called PEP or Prevent injury and Enhance Performance – lead researcher Dr. Bert Mandelbaum has observed that women, when landing from any type of propulsion, tend to be more upright when compared to men. As a result, extensive strain is placed on the ACL when the quadriceps muscle is activated in this extended or slightly flexed knee position. An important teaching strategy would be, for example, to instruct athletes to lower their center of gravity by flexing at the hips and knees during landing and cutting movements. The implication is that men and women need to be taught to move correctly. When they do, overall injury rates will likely be lowered.

While it must be acknowledged that anatomical, hormonal and proper technique (biomechanics) can impact injury rate, several studies have shown that adding functional – proprioceptive or neuromuscular training – to traditional approaches can significantly reduce the number of ACL injuries (Caraffa et al., 1996; Hewett et al., 1996; Hewett et al., 1999; reported in Smith, 2001). The PEP project advocates five sensible steps you can take to decrease knee injuries. Strategies include improving flexibility, increasing strength, avoiding positions that increase risk of injury because of poor biomechanics or known ortho-pedic concerns by teaching correct positioning or technique, using plyometric programs where specific and appropriate, and increasing proprioceptive stimuli through exercise that floods the proprioceptive and central nervous systems.

SPORT-SPECIFIC ACTIVITIES

Sport or occupational specific drills and exercise have an important place in rehabilitation, too. Sport specific movement, functional and closed chain exercise serve to "hard wire" the proprio-ceptive pathways in the central nervous system (CNS). Envision the "hard wire" connection as a sure and consistent pathway for efficient movement that results from solidifying movement blueprints in the CNS. You ingrain these patterns and learn them by using functional activity to transition skill and strength levels to a point where daily and sport movement patterns are handled easily. This is in contrast to a "wireless" connection, or training that is not specific, which is sure to fail at some point in relation to the training or rehabilitation goal. This type of "connection" often ends up failing because it produces inefficient physical carry over to daily life. Non-specific training is sure to cause "movement static!"

BODY MECHANICS & NEUTRAL SPINAL POSTURE

• • • • •

Functional movement, or the ability to move and respond without restriction, as well as to move and respond effectively and with intention, begins with an understanding of neutral spinal posture. Not only do you need to conceptualize neutral posture, but you must be able to move into, and out of, neutral spinal posture upon command. Think of neutral posture as a body awareness skill that should be mastered as soon as possible. Safe and effective alignment, dynamic movement and core conditioning are closely tied to understanding the "how" and "when" of neutral spinal posture.

NEUTRAL SPINAL POSTURE

Neutral posture can simply be defined as avoiding the extremes of sustained spinal flexion (rounded spine) or extension (arched spine), or positioning the spinal column and pelvis in a manner that reflects a mid-position between the extremes of these two joint actions. A total approach to abdominal and back strengthening, back wellness and balance training teaches the concept of neutral posture. Avoiding the extremes of sustained flexion and extension, when appropriate, should be taught for both the cervical (neck) and low back (lumbar) areas of the spine. Likewise, intentional movement away from neutral posture is not an issue of right or wrong, but one of appropriateness as related to movement demands.

Being able to set-up neutral posture when desired helps to conserve the integrity of spinal discs, ligaments and joint integrity, as well as enhancing movement capability. Awareness of neutral posture encourages a return to, or maintenance of, spinal alignment during daily tasks or sport movement.

Neutral spinal posture can, in a simplified manner, be defined as an absence of tension in the neck (cervical spine) or low back (lumbar spine). The strongest position of the spine and the position least likely to contribute to increased risk of injury or chronic degenerative spinal disease is represented by neutral posture. Neutral spinal posture refers to the maintenance of normal spinal curves that are inherent to a healthy, strong and properly aligned spine. (See Fig. A)

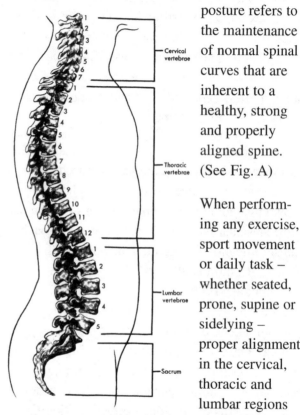

When performing any exercise, sport movement or daily task – whether seated, prone, supine or sidelying – proper alignment in the cervical, thoracic and lumbar regions should be considered. Decisions need to be made with regard to whether or not neutral spinal posture should be maintained (i.e., during a dynamic sporting activity or when performing trunk stability exercises), or if intentionally, the exerciser should choose to move out of neutral (i.e., performing trunk flexion which is typically referred to as a trunk curl or crunch exercise).

Fig. A Vertebral column exhibiting the normal curvatures inherent to a healthy and properly aligned spine.

It is critical to physical movement and back-health to have mastered the skill of freely and intentionally moving from and returning to neutral spinal posture, as well as maintaining spinal neutral throughout an exercise or movement when appropriate.

Neutral spinal posture is best illustrated by the maintenance of the cervical, thoracic and lumbar curves. (See Fig. B) It is important to observe the natural spinal curves and that the vertebrae are not stacked vertically upon one another. Yet, you can see through the preservation of the desired or normal curvatures of the spine, that this positioning protects the integrity of the spinal ligaments, joints and intervertebral discs. When the spine is neutral, the weight of the spine, gravity and other forces are equally distributed across the weight bearing surface of the discs and spinal joints, and are less likely to stress the functional units (the dynamic joints and supportive soft tissue structures) of the spine. Neutral posture minimizes compressive, shear and rotary torque forces.

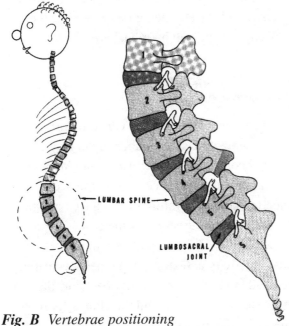

Fig. B *Vertebrae positioning in a neutral lumbar spine.*

Illustration adapted from Low Back Pain Syndrome, Rene Cailliet, M.D., F.A. Davis, 4th printing, 1991, pg. 4.

NEUTRAL POSTURE OF THE LUMBAR SPINE

There is not a widely accepted definition of "neutral lumbar posture" in reference to what is healthy, or "acceptable" versus "unacceptable." It would be inappropriate to categorize this posture reference as such because there are a wide range of pelvic/spinal positions that avoid the extremes of spinal flexion and extension that could be termed, or in fact represent, healthy or functional "neutral." Additionally, because a person possessed a "perfect" representation of anatomical neutral, does not mean the individual would never experience back pain or be at no risk for spinal degeneration or injury.

However, since the majority of people will fall in line with statistical likelihood, it still makes good sense from an anatomical/injury perspective to understand and strive for an improved neutral posture. Neutral posture can technically be described as a mid-position between the two extremes of maximum anterior tilt (arched back) and maximum posterior tilt (flat back). In addition, it is critical to remember that each individual has a given posture that is "normal" for her/him. The key is to identify the amount, if any, of normal lumbar spinal curvature. This identification procedure gives you a starting point for exercises, and an awareness of the position to return to after each repetition of an exercise, sustain through an exercise, or attempt to maintain throughout the day. The fitness professional should be able to determine a reference point for an "individual neutral" that is based on the person's current level of trunk strength, flexibility and ability to position the pelvis and spine. It is from this personal starting point that a person can choose to sustain, move away from neutral and/or return to this starting posture or neutral reference point. Neutral posture can change as strength and flexibility of key spinal muscles increase, or as the flexibility of key postural muscles (i.e., hamstrings and hip flexors) is improved, and as the individual becomes more skillful in her ability to sense and attain neutral positioning.

IDENTIFYING NEUTRAL LUMBAR POSTURE

In order to work with each individual's unique physical traits, it is helpful to teach the individual how to identify his/her unique neutral or natural lumbar spinal position.

One of the easiest ways to identify posture in the lumbar region is to stand with the heels close to or touching a wall. The protrusion of the buttocks and shoulder blades (scapulae) should lightly touch the wall. Attempt to slide one hand, palm facing the wall, between the small of the back and the wall surface. Many participants who have self-administered this evaluation find there is no space. Some find that two or three fingers may fit in nicely. Others, with significant lordosis, report that they can "drive a truck" through the existing space!

Regardless of curvature, as measured by how the hand or fingers fit into the lumbar space, this becomes the reference point for returning to neutral. It should be noted that external observance by a fitness professional should be just that, an observance. Diagnostic tools provided by a medical professional should be suggested if excessive curvature or lack of curvature give cause for concern. There is no "perfect" amount of curvature, nor is it within the scope-of-practice of most fitness professionals to try and attempt to ascertain whether a specific spinal curvature is desired, or represents an unhealthy situation.

Another method that can be used to identify neutral posture is to slowly rotate the pelvis into an anterior tilt (arching the low back) and then slowly rotate the pelvis into a posterior tilt (flattening the low back). Find a neutral point that represents a position between the two extremes. This method can effectively be used by placing the individual in a hands and knees position on the floor, a standing position with a slight bend in the knees against a wall, or by positioning the client in a seated position on a stability ball.

NEUTRAL POSTURE OF THE PELVIS

Pelvic posture is related to lumbar spinal posture. Moving or tilting the pelvis in an anterior or posterior position will result in flexion or extension of the lumbar spine. For many group exercise participants, clients and patients the idea of lumbar and pelvic neutral can be clarified by characterizing the pelvic bowl as a bucket full of water. Neutral pelvic position is represented by a full bucket of water that keeps its content intact. An anterior pelvic tilt (arched back) is represented by water spilling over the front edge of the pelvis or front brim of the bucket. A posterior pelvic tilt (flat back or spinal flexion) would be represented by water being splashed over the back edge of the pelvis or bucket.

NEUTRAL POSTURE OF THE CERVICAL SPINE

The major area of focus and concern during activity tends to be the lumbar spine. However, of equal concern is the cervical spine (neck). Neutral position of the cervical spine occurs when the head is comfortably balanced and the natural existing curvature of the cervical spine is maintained. There should be a minimum of muscle activity and stress in the neck. Generally, the head is neither forward nor back, or tilted to either side of the body, and the chin is level or parallel to the ground.

If you have questions or concerns about too much, or too little spinal curvature, consult with a licensed and appropriately trained health care professional. If indicated, there are strengthening and stretching exercises that may help a person with poor back or neck posture attain a more neutral and healthy position of the spine. In some extreme cases, the proper care may be temporarily out of your domain. Generally, if this is the case, you will become part of a team approach that meets the physical and medical needs of the individual.

TRUNK FLEXION AND EXTENSION

Early anatomy books illustrate that either excessive extension or flexion of the lumbar spine result in disproportionate and unequal stress on the discs located between the vertebrae. Over time such stress could result in herniated discs, and resultant swelling, nerve root irritation or impingement, and/or degeneration of the verte-brae. Sustaining a misalignment like this during dynamic movement or throughout the day (sitting with a rounded back), may cause irreparable and cumulative damage that can lead to pain, injury and a loss of mobility in the low back region.

Vertebral or spinal flexion is characterized by compression to the anterior aspect of the disc. Spinal flexion occurs when performing traditional abdominal or reverse "curls" where the rib is drawn toward the pelvis, or vice-versa, or when a person sits with a rounded low back at his desk. Posterior ligaments, the muscle sheath, and other soft tissue limit excessive flexion. (See Fig. C) Spinal extension is restricted by mechanical impact of the facet joints and by the anterior longitudinal ligament. (See Fig. D)

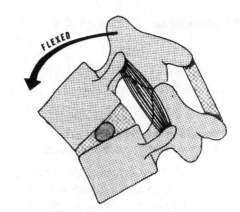

Fig. C Trunk Flexion

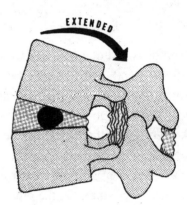

Fig. D Trunk Extension

Illustrations adapted from Low Back Pain Syndrome, Rene Cailliet, M.D., F.A. Davis, 4th printing, 1991, pg. 90.

When neutral alignment of the lumbar spine is maintained, the forces on the discs between the vertebrae are greatly reduced, as well as stretch forces to stabilizing spinal ligaments. Neutral posture more evenly spreads compression, shear or torque forces over the load bearing surfaces of the intervertebral discs. This helps avoid a concentration of high stress forces in small areas of the discs.

NEUTRAL POSTURE APPLICATION

In an extensive review, Plowman (1992) high-lights the importance of neutral spinal posture in the lumbar region. Greater posterior tilt (toward flat back position) increases low back muscle and ligament tension and, as a result, compression on the spine. It is reasonable to conclude that a sustained flexed or flat back position inherits many of the same risks that a sustained extended or excessively arched back does. Specifically, the ligaments, muscles, fascia and discs that make up the spinal column are put at risk for chronic, degenerative processes to occur.

It must be emphasized that the back was meant to flex as well as extend, and was meant to laterally flex and rotate. Keep in mind that you cannot perform effective, full range mover (or isolation) type trunk exercises without flexing or extending the spine. Nor can you effectively participate in athletic-type movement unless you move into, and out of, neutral posture. On the other hand, if you're sitting at a desk, driving your car, riding a stationary bike or walking you should ideally strive to preserve neutral spinal posture.

Flexion and extension are well tolerated by the spine and its associated soft tissues, including the spinal discs. In fact, this type of movement is necessary, for example, to achieve disc nutrition. Dynamic movement would not be possible if the spine did not tolerate this type of movement. However, excessive and uncontrolled (ballistic) movement of the spine, as well as rotation that is combined with a poorly aligned spine, can be detrimental. Remember that the devastating nature of back pain is not associated with a "lightening strike." Instead, a habit we might characterize as seemingly innocuous, such as sustaining poor seated posture over long periods of time, is a leading contributor to low back pain and discomfort.

*Note: Much of the information used in the previous section, **Body Mechanics**, was excerpted or adapted with permission from Effective Strength Training, by Douglas Brooks, 2000.*

THE IMPORTANCE OF WARMING UP & COOLING DOWN FOR NEUROMUSCULAR TRAINING

The warm-up and cool-down are both important and productive parts of *any* workout, and this is especially true when you're participating in functional or balance training. Your nerves and muscles will acclimate during a warm-up, which will enhance skill, performance and perception of personal success. A cool-down will return the body safely to a pre-exercise state.

PHYSIOLOGICAL BENEFITS OF WARM-UPS

Following are several possible mechanisms by which a warm-up could improve performance and sharpen neuromuscular responses as a result of increases in blood flow and increases in muscle and core temperature.

1. **PERMIT A GRADUAL INCREASE IN METABOLIC REQUIREMENTS.** Hemoglobin releases oxygen to the working muscles more readily at higher temperatures. This facilitates increased oxygen utilization (extraction) by the muscles, making physical performance more effective and efficient. This type of physiological response will not only enhance cardiorespiratory performance and reduce stress to the heart, but it will enhance all movement capabilities.

2. **PREVENT THE PREMATURE ONSET OF BLOOD LACTIC ACID ACCUMULATION AND PREMATURE FATIGUE.** A *progressive* warm-up keeps you from moving too quickly from low-intensity to high-intensity effort, and thus avoiding the consequences of doing so. Blood flow increases because higher temperatures in the body's core and its musculature cause vasodilation of the blood vessels. During

warm-up, blood travels from the body's core to the working muscles. More blood availability means more oxygen and nutrients to fuel exercise and muscle contraction, and efficient removal of metabolic byproduct production.

3. **CAUSE A GRADUAL INCREASE IN MUSCLE TEMPERATURE.** This reduces the likelihood of soft-tissue (muscle fascia or muscle) injury. Increased muscle temperature may also allow for greater mechanical (movement) efficiency because of lowered viscous resistance within the muscles. Viscosity (thickness) of the muscle protoplasm decreases, allowing the protein filaments (actin and myosin) of the muscle fibers to contract easily without resistance. Warm muscles move faster and generate force more effectively than "cold" muscles.

4. **ENHANCE NEURAL TRANSMISSION FOR MUSCLE CONTRACTION AND MOTOR-UNIT RECRUITMENT.** Motor skills improve at higher temperatures because nerve impulses travel faster. This enhances the speed of muscle contraction and force generated, along with muscle relaxation. Sports and activities that require coordination, reaction time and agility benefit greatly from a warm-up.

5. **PROVIDE AN "EARLY ALERT" FOR SCREENING POTENTIAL MUSCULOSKELETAL OR CARDIORESPIRATORY PROBLEMS.** Musculoskeletal weaknesses that predispose an individual to injury may worsen at higher intensities of exercise, and symptoms suggestive of chronic (i.e., heart disease) or other diseases that may, or may not, be diagnosed can present as exercise challenge increases.

If a questionable or high-risk situation arises it is prudent to stop the activity until any uncertainty is answered and the individual is cleared to return to exercise.

(References: Brooks, 1997, ACE Personal Trainer Manual, 1996; ACSM, 1995; McArdle et al., 1991; Giese, 1988.)

WARM-UP THEORY INTO PRACTICE

Balance training should begin only after a proper and thorough warm-up. It's obvious that warm-up accomplishes important changes in the body, which may reduce the risk of injury and improve performance. Graduated, low-level, and rhythmic, large muscle involvement is essential for creating a safe and effective warm-up. A warm-up for the BOSU Integrated Balance Training Workout should consist of three phases:

1. **ACCLIMATION.** It's important to acclimate to the dynamic surface of the BOSU dome before beginning any dynamic or static balance drills or exercises. Walking over the top of the dome, practicing mounting and dismounting in all directions, and introducing simple static and dynamic movements will help prepare the neuromuscular system for further balance challenges.

2. **GENERAL WARM-UP.** This should involve rhythmic and continuous movement, large-muscle group involvement and other exercises that are usually unrelated to the specific neuromuscular action of the drills that are to follow. The goal is to increase core temperature and gradually increase joint range of motion.

3. **ACTIVITY-SPECIFIC WARM-UP.** A skill rehearsal, often at a cadence that is slower than the drills to follow, reflects the specificity principle. Static and dynamic balance challenges, broken into individual parts, as

well as an introduction to proprioceptive tasks will prepare the neuromuscular system for compound movement with various force requirements.

Refer to the Warm-Up and Acclimation section of this manual, or to the BOSU Integrated Balance Training Video for specific exercises and drills.

PHYSIOLOGICAL BENEFITS OF COOL-DOWNS

Following are several possible mechanisms by which a cool-down could affect metabolism, as well as the neuromuscular and cardiovascular systems.

1. **HELPS IN FASTER REMOVAL OF LACTIC ACID AND LESSENS THE POTENTIAL FOR POST-EXERCISE MUSCLE SORENESS.**
   In normal exercise situations, lactic acid itself does not cause or contribute significantly to muscle soreness. Any soreness is probably a result of all-out or unaccustomed effort, and the resultant soft tissue damage. In the presence of oxygen during recovery or lessened intensity, lactic acid becomes an energy source. But high-intensity exercise *associated* with lactic acid production often *does* create delayed-onset muscle soreness (DOMS).

2. **REDUCE ANY TENDENCY TOWARD POST-EXERCISE FAINTING AND DIZZINESS.** The rhythmic "milking" action of muscular contraction and consequent compression of the veins is critical to ensure adequate venous return and reduce the likelihood of fainting or creating unnecessary stress to the heart. If blood is pooled in the lower extremities (venous pooling) from a sudden stop in exercise, the high hydrostatic forces cause a decreased venous return and blood pressure declines. At the same time, the heart rate

accelerates, which means the heart muscle needs more blood and oxygen at a time when its supply may be compromised.

3. **MAY REDUCE THE LIKELIHOOD OF SOME MUSCLE SORENESS IF STRETCHING IS ADDED.** By preventing muscle spasms or involuntary contractions of the muscles, soreness may be reduced.

4. **HELP LOWER BLOOD LEVELS OF ADRENALINE.** Adrenaline that lingers in the bloodstream can stress the heart. The continuation of mild exercise into recovery may minimize any possible negative effects on heart function because of elevated catecholamines epinephrine and norepinephrine. These adrenaline-like hormones affect the body's response to increasing quantity and intensity of exercise, and it is observed that their levels increase after exercise (McArdle et al., 1991; Dimsdale, 1987).

COOL-DOWN THEORY INTO PRACTICE

An active cool-down of moderate to mild exercise means that you *continue* exercising at an intensity which is lower than the high intensity segments of the workout. This level will facilitate blood flow through the vascular network (including the heart) during recovery. A cool-down for the BOSU Integrated Balance Training Workout could consist of low-level, rhythmic activity that allows the body to reverse the blood shunt, or shift, that occurred as the workout began, and helps to ensure adequate blood flow to the working muscles and other body systems.

Sequencing a workout with cardiovascular or athletic conditioning drills alternated with muscular strength, endurance and stabilization drills, will vary the intensity and facilitate cooling down and stretching when desired. A reduction of exercise intensity will be reflected by the return of the exercise heart rate to lower levels and eventually to a resting heart-rate level. A "quick" recovery is dependent on current fitness level, the intensity of effort for the preceding workout, and the intensity of the cool-down activity.

Warm-up and cool-down not only reduce the potential for premature fatigue and post-exercise fatigue, they reduce the risk of exercise-related injuries as well. Because exercise may "feel" more comfortable and be less of a stress to the body after warming up and cooling down, both of these factors can contribute to high levels of motivation and consequent exercise compliance.

TEACHING BOSU
INTEGRATED BALANCE TRAINING

BOSU programming, exercises and drills focus on training movements, or groups of muscles working together to produce coordinated movement. Indeed, this may be the paradigm *shift* that is needed to introduce a balanced approach to training. Though traditional approaches can focus too much on isolating muscles, note the emphasis is on a paradigm "shift." This speaks of a change which is not an all-or-none approach, or that singles out one type of training as "best." Instead, this category of training helps to complete your approach to successfully presenting a program that covers all necessary facets of health, fitness and sport. Generally, fitness enthusiasts and athletes who have superior balance skills and excellent sense of body and joint position, learn sport skills more easily and respond to movement-training (i.e., skill acquisition) more quickly.

Keep the following teaching considerations in mind and you will find that varying ages and fitness levels, and different types of people with various physical conditions can use the BOSU Balance Trainer. However, individuals with hip replacements, high blood pressure, visual or balance impairments, or other conditions which may cause safety concerns, should be referred to a qualified health professional.

PROGRESSING BALANCE TRAINING MOVEMENT

Though an exact protocol for exercise selection and progression does not exist for each individual or group exercise scenario, the following guidelines will help you to create appropriate class or individual workout programming. Generally, exercises should be progressed from static to dynamic movement, from relatively stable to more unstable movement and from simple to complex movement.

STATIC TO DYNAMIC MOVEMENT

As is emphasized in the exercise section of this manual and demonstrated in the BOSU Integrated Balance Training video, movement challenges should move from static positions and holds, and/or very simple rhythmic movements performed with control, to more dynamic or challenging movement. Static postures include single- or double-leg standing, kneeling, seated, sidelying, supine and prone positions, where movement is limited. Also appropriate are basic movements that include stepping onto and off of the dome, moving across and/or performing compressions on top of the dome. Standing static balance and basic movement patterns can be thought of as positions or movements performed with a goal of maintaining a body position where the center of mass (your hips) remains positioned directly over the base of support (your feet).

After controlled balance is established in various static postures and simple movement patterns, it is appropriate to add more complex movement patterns and balance challenges. This type of movement includes skills such as compressions performed on top of the dome, and progresses to walking, running, jumping, leaping or otherwise moving onto and off of the dome in more dynamic fashion. Other simple skills/movements such as squats, lunges, reaching or following a moving body part with your eyes (visual tracking) while stabilizing and maintaining control can also be introduced. Dynamic balance incorporates balance and proprioceptive challenges while the body is in motion. After control and a sense of body awareness is established during dynamic movement, small range of motion can be progressed to greater range of motion, movements can be performed more quickly, different planes of movement can be explored, and proprioceptive tasks such as visual tracking can be added.

RELATIVELY UNSTABLE TO MORE UNSTABLE MOVEMENT

Stability challenges can be progressed with more difficult variations, or modified to easier variations, depending upon how the body is positioned. It is a "given" that the dome is an unstable surface, but a wide stance is more stable than a narrow stance and standing on one foot or kneeling on one knee, is more of a balance challenge when compared to standing on both feet or kneeling on both knees. Using a side touch to stabilize a standing or kneeling position while on the dome, or moving the hands overhead, a knee or foot out to the side, or moving the torso up or down versus keeping it "quiet," represent examples of increased or decreased stability challenges. Individuals can also practice movement on a solid surface (the floor is more stable) or dense mat (more challenging than the floor, but easier than the dome), and then move to the dome. Exercises can be performed in front of a mirror if available, but should eventually progress to using no mirror. When a mirror is used, balance becomes much easier because of visual feedback and helps individuals with less body awareness establish a visual picture of correct technique, which they can store in the brain and the muscles. This new and correct motor memory comes into play, for example, when the mirror is no longer used, or when closing one or both eyes challenges stability.

SIMPLE TO MORE COMPLEX MOVEMENT

If in doubt, progressions or movement sequences should err on the side of being too easy!

Movement that progresses from static to dynamic, to multiple- and varied-plane variations, as well as exercise that moves from single- to multi-task challenges assures excellent technique, form, and participant safety, as well as a sense of accomplishment and self esteem by anyone who participates. Your ability at assessing how the session or group class is progressing in terms of personal success is very important. You may have to change class or session direction by slowing down or advancing the progressions, depending on how the individual or group is reacting. Class or session direction should change, for example, when frustration or fatigue becomes apparent. When the central nervous system becomes fatigued – balance and sport performance, as well as any physical task and the skills required to perform them – greatly diminishes. At the risk of redundancy, you cannot progress too slowly or keep the movement challenges too simple, especially in the early stages of this type of training!

INTRODUCING BOSU MODULES

In the BOSU Balance Training Workout Video, groups of drills and exercises are sequenced together in modules (of approximately 10 – 15 minutes in length) with a specific training goal in mind. Types of modules that can be created include:

- Warm-up and acclimation
- Core conditioning
- General athletic conditioning
- Sport specific conditioning
- Static balance training
- Dynamic balance training
- Winter sports conditioning
- Rhythmic conditioning
- Flexibility and relaxation

Learning new motor patterns and balance skills can either be fun, challenging, exciting and encouraging or depressing, difficult and discouraging. Regardless, learning and training new neuromuscular responses takes time. As mentioned, progression of movements and more difficult variations cannot occur too slowly. Therefore, with new participants, be sure to use an acclimation module where the individuals can "get a feel for" or otherwise receive an introduction to the air filled dome. It is important to develop a kinesthetic relationship by contact. Acclimation modules can always be used for warm-up, regardless of the participant's previous experience.

Acclimation modules, and the progressions within, teach proper posture and body alignment, begin to develop body and balance awareness or re-orient the experienced participant to the dynamic surface of the dome. Proper sequencing of different exercise modules, including the acclimation modules, should challenge balance with static and then more dynamic progressions. Be sure to include enough of both static and dynamic movement challenges, and target not only full body balance challenges, but focus on upper body, lower body and core/trunk drills, too. Finally, help participants to use "internal cues" to succeed. Use posture checks, subtle weight shifts and visualization, for example, to keep them focused on balance and in tune with their bodies during the training.

If you're using music and exercising to the musical phrase, it's a good idea to introduce BOSU training in the initial acclimation module without attempting to stay on the beat or phrase, or forgo the music all together. This will allow participants to get used to the dynamic characteristic of the dome, practice stepping on and off of the dome, build confidence and skill, and learn to move efficiently and safely on the BOSU at a self-directed pace.

Avoid unnecessary soreness by limiting BOSU workouts initially to 2-3 times per week, or by using balance training for 10-15 minute time periods. Functional training is a new experience for many people so the muscles and soft tissues will not be accustomed to this new "load." Basic conditioning and skill development should occur before advanced conditioning and skill development (you shouldn't try a 360 degree jump turn your first time on the BOSU)! Provide modifications and progressions that accommodate any physical limitations. This will keep the exercise safe and limit potential participant frustration.

Proper progression will often dictate whether the experience is perceived in a negative or positive light. The paradox of BOSU training is that any person, regardless of age or fitness level, can experience immediate success on the balance trainer. The contradiction lies in the ability of the BOSU Balance Trainer to offer progressive challenges that few people will ever completely master. Therein lies the caution. BOSU training can always present a challenge that is unattainable. Some people, dependent upon when that challenge is introduced, can find the experience inappropriate and frustrating, or very rewarding, satisfying and motivating!

COMMONLY ASKED QUESTIONS
& INFLATION INSTRUCTIONS

1. WHY BOSU?

BOSU is one of the most exciting, fresh, and challenging pieces of fitness equipment to hit the fitness industry in years. Though validated by sports professionals, BOSU training is for everyone. Professional and Olympic teams from virtually every sport, as well as fitness and health professionals world-wide, are using this incredibly effective functional training device. BOSU balance training can help to develop core stability, proprioception and balance. BOSU is multidimensional as it can be used within any component of fitness, complement other fitness products, or it can stand alone.

2. HOW SAFE IS THE BOSU WORKOUT?

BOSU exercises and progressions are designed with safety in mind. The effectiveness of any exercise is carefully weighed against any safety issues. It is easy to step off BOSU in any direction when balance is challenged, and the domed surface of the BOSU helps to minimize high impact, repetitive forces. Individuals with varying levels of fitness can participate without having an increased risk for injury. Each fitness and health professional who uses the BOSU to train clients, group exercise participants or patients will need to look at the risk/effectiveness ratio for each exercise or drill, with regard to the individual's (or group's) needs and goals.

3. WHAT SPACE REQUIREMENTS ARE NECESSARY FOR A BOSU WORKOUT?

Each participant should have enough space to lie in a prone, supine or sidelying position on top of the dome, and to be able to step off safely in any direction. This equates to about 12 to 16 square feet of space, which is similar to the space allotment for a step platform in a group exercise setting.

4. WHAT TYPE OF FLOOR SURFACE IS BEST FOR A BOSU WORKOUT?

The BOSU can be placed on any level surface. Low-pile carpeting, rubber flooring or wood surfaces work best. If working out on a wood or other hard surface, a mat or folded towel can provide padding when exercises are performed with the knees or hands in contact with the floor.

5. DOES SWEAT MAKE THE BOSU SURFACE SLIPPERY?

Yes. And, you will sweat! Not unlike a wet basketball floor, sweat will make the dome surface of the BOSU slippery. Wearing appropriate athletic footwear can help minimize slippage. It's important to regularly use a hand towel during a class or training session to wipe off the dome and the surrounding floor if necessary. A dry BOSU provides for a safer and more effective training environment. Hygiene issues are minimized as well.

6. WHAT SHOULD I WEAR WHEN WORKING OUT ON BOSU?

Footwear. *Though not required, it is recommended that athletic footwear be worn during BOSU workouts. Keep your workout shoes clean and free of abrasive material. Not only will proper footwear lessen slippage concerns, but the foot will be properly supported. Additionally, there is the possibility that if the BOSU is not properly inflated, compression of the dome could result in the foot contacting the rim of the platform. More dynamic and advanced jumping- or twisting-type movements could also result in foot contact with the platform rim. While this type of contact is not harmful to your BOSU, it could bruise the foot or cause other injury. If you choose not to wear athletic footwear, bare feet will provide the best contact with the dome, when compared to wearing socks.*

Clothing. *Comfortable clothing that does not slip or slide will allow more effective and safe movement, especially when in a prone, supine, seated or sidelying position on the dome. Nylon track-suits and running shorts that ride up the legs are examples of apparel choices that could frustrate you because this type of clothing may thwart smooth and comfortable movement in certain positions.*

7. HOW IS THE BOSU STORED?

Mobile Fitness Professionals. *Fitness and health professionals who travel to clients or patients, (personal trainers, athletic trainers (ATCs) or physical therapists) can quickly inflate and deflate the dome. This makes it easy and convenient to carry one or more BOSUs in any vehicle. If you leave or store BOSU units in a vehicle it is important to deflate the dome. Excessive heat can deform the dome when inflated, if the BOSU is left in direct sunlight or a hot environment such as a car trunk. Though the product can continue to be used, deformation may cause the original balance traits of the dome to change.*

Group Fitness. *In a group fitness setting, BOSUs readily stack three to four high. Twelve units can be stored in 16 square feet. BOSU units easily store along any wall, and other stacking configurations are possible. DO NOT STORE THE BOSU BALANCE TRAINER IN DIRECT SUNLIGHT WHEN INFLATED. Direct sunlight can cause the inflated dome to deform. Though the product can continue to be used, deformation may cause the original balance traits of the dome to change.*

8. HOW DURABLE IS THE BOSU?

BOSU's high-quality vinyl has been tested to be burst resistant at 2800 pounds. Proper care and storage will impact its lifetime. Inflate your BOSU properly and avoid contact with sharp objects. Store the BOSU away from direct sunlight and sources of heat. If BOSU is stored in a car, deflate the dome and keep the unit out of direct sunlight. BOSU units stored in a club environment should be stacked so that they are out of contact with direct sunlight or heat sources. Clean the BOSU with water and/or a mild soap.

9. HOW IS THE BOSU INFLATED?

A pump comes with your BOSU and inflating the BOSU is easy. Tip the platform up on its side or place it on your lap. Press against the center of the vinyl and hold the valve housing in place. Insert the pump nozzle firmly and begin to inflate. Inflate your BOSU until the dome feels firm to touch. It's a good idea to lubricate the plug with Vaseline or other petroleum based lubricant. Lubricating the dome plug will facilitate easy insertion and removal. For more information, refer to the written inflation instructions that came with your BOSU.

REFERENCES & BIBLIOGRAPHY

· · · · ·

American College of Sports Medicine--ACSM (1998). The recommended quantity and quality of exercise for developing and maintaining cardiorespiratory and muscular fitness, and flexibility in healthy adults. Position stand. *Medicine and Science in Sports and Exercise*; Vol. 30, pgs. 975-91.

American College of Sports Medicine (ACSM). (1998). *ACSM Resource Manual for Guidelines for Exercise Testing and Prescription*; 3rd edition. Baltimore, MD: Williams and Wilkins.

American College of Sports Medicine (ACSM). (1997). *Exercise Management for Persons With Chronic Diseases and Disabilities*. L. Durstine (Ed.). Champaign IL: Human Kinetics.

American College of Sports Medicine (ACSM). (1995). *ACSM Guidelines For Exercise Testing and Prescription*; 5th edition. Philadelphia, PA: Williams and Wilkins.

Basmajian, John and DeLuca, Carlo (1979). *Muscles Alive - Their Functions Revealed By Electromyography*. 4th edition, Williams and Wilkins, Baltimore, MD.

Beynnon, B.D., Fleming, B.C., Johnson, R.J., et al (1995). *Anterior cruciate ligament strain behavior during rehabilitation exercises in vivo*. American Journal of Sports Medicine; Vol. 23, No. 1, pgs. 24-34.

Beynnon, B.D., Johnson, R.J., Fleming, B.C., et al (1997). *The strain behavior of the anterior cruciate ligament during squatting and active flexion-extension: a comparison of an open and a closed kinetic chain exercise*. American Journal of Sports Medicine; Vol. 25, No. 6, pgs. 823-829.

Blievernicht, John (1998). *Balance Training*. IDEA Personal Trainer. September.

Bompa, Tudor (1999). *Periodization: Training for Sports*. Human Kinetics: Champaign, IL.

Bompa, Tudor (1996). *Periodization of Strength*. Veritas Publishing, Inc.: Toronto, Canada.

BOSU Balance Trainer Web Site can be visited at www.bosupro.com. BOSU educational training manuals, videos and the BOSU Balance Trainer can be ordered online, or by calling 1-800-321-9236, M-F 9:30 - 4:30 E.T.

Brooks, Douglas (2001). *Effective Strength Training: Analysis and Technique for the Upper Body, Lower Body and Trunk Exercises*. Moves International Fitness: Mammoth Lakes, CA (760) 934-0312 and Human Kinetics: Champaign, IL.

Brooks, Douglas (1999). *Conditioning for Winter Sports*. IDEA Personal Trainer; June, pgs. 26-36.

Brooks, Douglas (1997). *Program Design for Personal Trainers*. Moves International Fitness: Mammoth Lakes, CA and Human Kinetics: Champaign, IL.

Brooks, Douglas and Copeland, Candice (1997). *Total Stretch On The Ball – Stability Ball Training Guide For Fitness Professionals*. Moves International Fitness, Mammoth Lakes, CA (760) 934-0312.

Brooks, Douglas et al., (1995). *Total Strength On The Ball – Stability Ball Basic Training Guide For Fitness Professionals*. Moves International Fitness: Mammoth Lakes, CA (760) 934-0312.

Cailliet, Rene (1988). *Low Back Pain Syndrome*. 4th edition, F.A. Davis Company, Philadelphia, PA.

Chasan, Neil (2000). *Exercises for Golf's Long Game*. IDEA Personal Trainer. June.

Esenkaya, I., Tuygun, H., Turkmen, M.I., (2000). *Bilateral Anterior Shoulder Dislocation in a Weight Lifter*. The Physician and Sports Medicine; Vol. 28, No. 3, March, pgs: 93-100.

Feigenbaum, M.S., and Pollock, M.L., (1997). *Strength Training: Rationale for Current Guidelines for Adult Fitness Programs*. Physician and Sports Medicine; Vol. 25, pgs. 44-64.

Fleck, Steven and Kraemer, William (1996). *Periodization Breakthrough!* Advanced Research Press: Ronkonkoma, NY.

Fleck, Steven and Kraemer, William (1997). *Designing Resistance Training Programs*. Human Kinetics Publishers, Champaign, IL.

Freedson, Patty (2000). *Strength Training for Women*. IDEA Personal Trainer, July-August.

Frontera, W.R. et al (1988). *Strength Conditioning in Older Men: Skeletal Muscle Hypertrophy and Improved Function*. Palo Alto, CA: American Physiological Society.

Gross, M.L., Brenner, S.L., Esformes, I., et al., (1993). *Anterior shoulder instability in weight lifters*. American Journal of Sports Medicine; Vol 21, No. 4, pgs. 599-603.

Howley E., and Franks B. (1997). *Health and Fitness Instructors Handbook* (3rd. ed.). Champaign, IL: Human Kinetics.

Jones, Chester et al., (2000). *Weight Training Injury Trends: A 20-year survey*. The Physician and Sports Medicine; Vol. 28, No. 7, July, pgs. 61-72.

Kendall, Florence, et al., (1993). *Muscles - Testing and Function*. 4th edition, Williams and Wilkins, Baltimore, MD.

Komi, P.V., editor (1992). *Strength and Power in Sport*. Distributed by Human Kinetics Publishers, Champaign, IL.

Kravitz, Len (2001). *Low-Back Stability Training*. IDEA Personal Trainer. October.

Kujala, U.M., Kettunen, J., Paananen, H. (1995). *Knee osteoarthritis in former runners, soccer players, weight lifters, and shooters*. Arthritis Rheum; Vol. 38, No. 4, pgs. 539-546.

Laskowski, Edward, Newcomer-Aney, Karen and Smith, Jay (1997). *Refining rehabilitation with proprioception training*. Physician and Sports Medicine; Vol. 25, No. 10, October, pgs. 89-102.

Mazzeo, R.S., Cavanagh, P., and Evans, W. J., et al (1998). *ACSM Position Stand on Exercise and Physical Activity for Older Adults*. Medicine and Science in Sports and Exercise; Vol. 30, No. 6, pgs. 992-1008

McArdle, William et al., (1996). *Exercise Physiology - Energy, Nutrition, and Human Performance.* 4th edition, Lea & Febiger, Philadelphia, PA.

McGill, S. M. (2001). *Low-back stability: From formal description to issues for performance and rehabilitation.* Exercise and Sports Sciences Reviews; Vol. 29, No. 1, pgs. 26-31.

McLaughlin, Peter (2001). *The New Happy Hour: Make Fitness Fun.* IDEA Health and Fitness Source; March, pgs. 24-28.

Moves International Fitness is dedicated to and provides quality fitness education and related products. The BOSU Balance Trainer, as well as BOSU manuals, videos and home study courses can be ordered by calling (760) 934-0312, (800) 272-5055 or visiting their web site at **www.MovesIntFitness.com**

Palmitier, R.A., An K.N., Scott, S.G., et al (1991). *Kinetic chain exercise in knee rehabilitation.* Sports Medicine; Vo. 11, No. 6, pgs. 402-413.

Plowman, Sharon and Smith, Denise (1997). *Exercise Physiology for Health, Fitness and Performance.* Needham Heights, MA: Allyn and Bacon.

Plowman, Sharon (1992). *Physical Activity, Physical Fitness, and Low Back Pain.* Exercise and Sport Sciences Reviews; Vol. 20, pgs. 221-242.

Pollock, M. L., and G.A. Gaesser et al., (1998). *The recommended quantity and quality of exercise for developing and maintaining cardiorespiratory fitness, and flexibility in healthy adults.* Medicine and Science in Sports and Exercise; Vol. 30, No. 6, pgs. 975-991.

Post, William R. (1998). *Patellofemoral Pain, Physician and Sports Medicine.* Vol. 26, No. 1, pgs. 68-78, January.

Reeves, Ronald K., Edward R. Laskowski, and Jay Smith (1998). *Weight Training Injuries – Part I: Diagnosing and Managing Acute Conditions.* The Physician and Sports Medicine; Vol. 26, No. 2, pgs. 67-83, February.

Reeves, Ronald K., Edward R. Laskowski, and Jay Smith (1998). *Weight Training Injuries – Part II: Diagnosing and Managing Chronic Conditions.* The Physician and SportsMedicine; Vol. 26, No. 3, pgs. 54-63, March.

Salis, Robert E., Editor (2000). *Pearls – Stay In A Safe Rotator Cuff Range.* The Physician and Sportsmedicine; Vol. 28, No. 6, June, pg. 23.

Smith, Carrie Myers (2001). *Protecting the ACL.* IDEA Health and Fitness Source; January, pgs. 20-23.

Steinkamp, L.A., Dillingham, M.F., Markel, M.D., et al (1993). *Biomechanical considerations in patellofemoral joint rehabilitation.* American Journal of Sports Medicine; Vol. 21, No. 3, pgs. 438-444.

Shrier, Ian and Gossal, Kav (2000). *Myths and Truths of Stretching.* The Physician and Sports Medicine; August, pgs. 57-63.

Westcott, Wayne (1997). *Spring Training.* IDEA Personal Trainer, March/April, pgs. 26-27.

Westcott, W., F. Dolan and T. Cavicchi (1996). *Golf and Strength Training Are Compatible Activities.* Strength and Conditioning Vol. 18, No.4, pgs. 54-56.

Wilmore, Jack and Costill, David (1994). *Physiology of Sport and Exercise.* Human Kinetics: Champaign, IL.

Wolf, Chuck (2001). *Moving The Body.* IDEA Personal Trainer. June.

INTEGRATED BALANCE
TRAINING EXERCISES

In the following section you'll experience a wide spectrum of exercises, stretches and drills. They will range from simple to complex, and from low intensity to higher intensity. Guidelines and variations are described for each exercise, allowing you to choose the ones that are most appropriate for your own use or for the clientele or group fitness participants you work with. Remember, every exercise won't work for every person. It's up to you, the professional, to determine which exercises and drills will be most effective, based on the participant's goals and limitations.

Many of the following exercises and drills have two or three variations. The variations described first are generally the easiest to perform. When the first variation can be performed with proper technique and alignment, proceed to the subsequent variations, which generally require more balance, stabilization, proprioceptive skill, strength or flexibility. All unilateral exercises and stretches should be performed on both sides of the body.

For more information on sequencing, transitioning and progressing exercises, refer to the companion video, *BOSU Integrated Balance Training*.

INTEGRATED BALANCE TRAINING EXERCISES

ACCLIMATION & WARM-UP

● ● ● ● ●

MOUNT AND DISMOUNT

EXERCISE GOAL: The goal of these exercises is to acclimate to the dynamic surface of the BOSU dome, and to practice stepping on and off the dome in all directions.

SETUP AND ALIGNMENT: Stand on the floor with good, upright posture and neutral spinal alignment. Face the dome, with the toes approximately 6 to 12 inches from the platform.

PERFORMING THE EXERCISE: Place one foot in the center of the dome and step up (See Fig. 1). Pause when the body is centered over the supporting leg, then continue "walking over" the dome and onto the floor on the other side (See Fig. 2). Turn around and walk back over the dome, leading with the opposite leg. Repeat this walk over the top, changing legs each time, until the body has acclimated to the inflation level and the dynamic movement that occurs each time body weight is placed on the dome. When comfortable with walking over the dome, stand on top of the dome with the weight centered. Practice stepping off and back on the dome from all directions.

SAFETY CONSIDERATIONS: The foot of the supporting leg should be as level as possible when standing on the dome. Avoid excessive dorsi flexion, plantar flexion, inversion or eversion. The trailing leg should come forward and step down to the floor with little impact. When stepping off in a backward direction, the shoulders should stay aligned over the hips as the body lowers with control (See Fig. 3). Do not lean back while stepping to the back. Maintain neutral spinal alignment through both the mount and dismount phase. It is not recommended to step off in a forward direction, and then step backwards and up onto the dome. Always step up from a side or forward facing position.

Fig. 3

VARIATIONS AND COMMENTS: There are many variations that can be performed to practice the mount and dismount. Some examples are:

1) Walk over the top and pause with both feet together on top of the dome, then step forward and down with either leg. Turn around and repeat in the other direction.

2) Stand with the BOSU to one side of the body and side step over the dome. Step up just past the center of the dome with the inside leg, then step up with the other leg (feet are now centered on top of the dome). Step down to the side with the lead leg, then tap down with the foot of the trailing leg. Repeat this side traveling, over the dome, movement in the other direction.

3) Step up and down while traveling in an "L" configuration. Step up from the side, step down to the back, step up forward, and down to the other side.

Fig. 1   Fig. 2

EXERCISE GOAL: The goal of these exercises is to practice "centered" position, with and without proprioceptive tasks, which will challenge core stabilization, foot and ankle stabilization, and balance related to the vestibular system.

SETUP AND ALIGNMENT: Stand on top of the dome with the feet about hip width apart or slightly narrower. Place the arms out to the sides at about waist height for balance assistance, or place the hands on the hips for more balance challenge.

PERFORMING THE EXERCISE: Flex the knees slightly and maintain this "soft knee" position. Adjust spinal alignment so that neutral posture can be maintained in the lumbar and cervical spine. Retract the scapulae slightly to stabilize the shoulder girdle region. Keep the pelvis and shoulders level, avoiding excessive tilt in any direction (See Fig. 4). The body should be as "quiet" as possible, and ready to move in any direction. This stance will be referred to as "centered" position.

Fig. 4

SAFETY CONSIDERATIONS: Attempt to maintain level foot positioning when standing on the dome. Avoid excessive dorsi flexion, plantar flexion, inversion or eversion. The knees should remain "soft" or flexed slightly, rather than locked in a hyperextended position. Be aware of cervical spinal alignment. Don't push the head forward and tense the neck muscles. Co-contraction of the abdominal and lumbar spinal muscles will provide core stabilization and help avoid excessive lumbar flexion and extension while attempting to maintain balance.

VARIATIONS AND COMMENTS: To add further balance and stabilization challenge, close the eyes while standing in "centered" position (See Fig. 5). At first, just a few seconds will be difficult because of the lack of visual feedback. Gradually build up to 30 to 60 seconds of balance with closed eyes. When the eyes are closed, visualize correct body positioning on the dome and attempt to correct any misalignments. The lower legs, ankles and feet will be very active while balancing with closed eyes. Attempt to keep the trunk aligned, and avoid tipping the shoulders side to side.

Fig. 5

These balance and core stabilization exercises can be performed during any part of a workout. They are not limited to a warm-up segment. If the stabilizing muscles of the feet feel excessively fatigued, alternating leg compressions may be used as a recovery between tasks.

EXERCISE GOAL: The goal of these exercises is to practice "centered" position, with proprioceptive tasks, which will challenge core stabilization, foot and ankle stabilization, and balance related to the vestibular system.

SETUP AND ALIGNMENT: Stand on top of the dome in "centered" position. Place the arms out to the sides at about waist height for balance assistance, or place the hands on the hips for more balance challenge.

PERFORMING THE EXERCISE: Flex the knees slightly and maintain this "soft knee" position. Adjust spinal alignment so that neutral posture can be maintained in the lumbar and cervical spine. Retract the scapulae slightly to stabilize the shoulder girdle region. Keep the pelvis and shoulders level, avoiding excessive tilt in any direction.

Fig. 6

Slowly turn the head to one side until the chin is facing the shoulder (See Fig. 6). Return the head to the center, then turn in the other direction. Repeat, or combine this exercise with other proprioceptive tasks.

SAFETY CONSIDERATIONS: When adding head movements, such as turning side to side, begin with small range of motion and progress to greater range of motion. Do not exceed a range of motion where "centered" position and good spinal alignment cannot be maintained. Attempt to maintain level foot positioning on the dome. Avoid excessive dorsi flexion, plantar flexion, inversion or eversion. The knees should be "soft" or flexed slightly, rather than locked in a hyperextended position.

VARIATIONS AND COMMENTS: To add further balance and stabilization challenge, slowly tilt the head to one side until the ear is facing the top of the shoulder (See Fig. 7). Return the head to an upright position, then tilt in the other direction. While tilting the head, visualize correct body positioning on the dome and attempt to correct any misalignments. Turning or tilting the head side to side with the eyes *closed* will present a very advanced balance challenge.

Fig. 7

These balance and core stabilization exercises can be performed during any part of a workout. They are not limited to a warm-up segment. If the stabilizing muscles of the feet feel excessively fatigued, alternating leg compressions may be used as a recovery between tasks.

EXERCISE GOAL: The goal of these exercises is to challenge static balance, core stabilization, and foot and ankle stabilization.

SETUP AND ALIGNMENT: Stand on top of the dome in "centered" position. Place one foot in the middle of the dome and shift all the weight onto this foot (See Fig. 8). The arms may be extended out to the sides at about waist height for balance assistance, or the hands may rest on the hips for more balance challenge.

Fig. 8   Fig. 9

PERFORMING THE EXERCISE: With the weight bearing leg centered on the top of the dome, place the inside of the other foot against the side of the dome (See Fig. 9). Keep the toes or inner foot against the dome for balance assistance, and adjust posture and spinal alignment. Lift the foot away from the dome slightly to test balance and stabilization. Hold this balanced position for 10 to 60 seconds. Then, bring the leg onto the top of the dome, shift the weight onto the other foot and repeat the balance on the other side.

SAFETY CONSIDERATIONS: Attempt to maintain level foot positioning when standing on the dome. Avoid excessive dorsi flexion, plantar flexion, inversion or eversion. The knee of the weight bearing leg should be "soft" or flexed slightly, rather than locked in a hyperextended position. Maintain neutral spinal alignment, and avoid tipping the shoulders and pelvis to either side while the weight is on one leg. Contracting the core musculature will enhance balance performance.

VARIATIONS AND COMMENTS: For further balance challenge, abduct the leg to the highest point where proper alignment ("centered" position) can be maintained with the spine, shoulders, pelvis and weight-bearing foot (See Fig. 10).

While performing static balances such as a single leg balance, the body should be "quiet" but dynamic. Avoid any movement that is not necessary to maintain or correct balance. As skill level improves and stabilizing muscles strengthen, the body will use less and less movement to maintain the balance.

Fig. 10

EXERCISE GOAL: The goal of these exercises is to practice dynamic balance while performing a variety of movement patterns. These movement patterns will challenge core stabilization, as well as hip, leg and ankle stabilization.

SETUP AND ALIGNMENT: Stand on top of the dome in "centered" position. Place the arms out to the sides at about waist height for balance assistance, or place the hands on the hips for more balance challenge.

PERFORMING THE EXERCISE: Flex the knees slightly and maintain this "soft knee" position. Adjust spinal alignment so that neutral posture can be maintained in the lumbar and cervical spine. Retract the scapulae slightly to stabilize the shoulder girdle region. Keep the pelvis and shoulders level, avoiding excessive tilt in any direction. Slowly shift the weight forward into the toes (See Fig. 11). Then, shift the weight back into the heels. Return to "centered" position and shift the weight onto one foot, then the other (See Fig. 12). Hold each position for a few seconds.

SAFETY CONSIDERATIONS: As the body weight shifts to the front, back or sides of the feet, maintain correct spinal alignment. Move smoothly from position to position without excessive reaction from the trunk or upper body. Begin the weight shifting movements with small range of motion, then increase range of motion as skill level, balance and control improve. Practicing weight shifting in all directions will improve the skill of maintaining level foot placement on top of the dome.

VARIATIONS AND COMMENTS: For more dynamic balance challenge, compound joint movement patterns may be performed. Flex at the hips and knees and perform a squat movement. The depth of the squat should be determined by proper alignment, balance and the ability to control the movement. Begin by touching the knees during the squat, then progress to touching the shins, ankles or dome. Return to "centered" position between each squat. The squat/touch can also be performed with trunk rotation (See Fig. 13). Rotating the trunk and tracking the hand touch on the knee, calf, ankle or dome will add both dynamic movement and vestibular challenge.

Fig. 11 *Fig. 12*

Fig. 13

EXERCISE GOAL: The goal of this group of exercises is to practice dynamic balance while performing head and arm visual tracking patterns. These movement patterns will challenge core stabilization, hip, leg and ankle stabilization, and balance related to the vestibular system.

SETUP AND ALIGNMENT: Stand on top of the dome in "centered" position. Let the arms hang naturally at the sides of the body.

PERFORMING THE EXERCISE: Flex the knees slightly and maintain this "soft knee" position. Adjust spinal alignment so that neutral posture can be maintained in the lumbar and cervical spine. Retract the scapulae slightly to stabilize the shoulder girdle region. Keep the pelvis and shoulders level, avoiding excessive tilt in any direction. Slowly lift the arms overhead, without changing body alignment. Lower the arms down and extend them behind the body. Lift one arm overhead and simultaneously extend the other arm back (See Fig. 14). Repeat arm movement patterns through different planes of movement, working both symmetrically and asymmetrically. For more balance challenge, add visual tracking by following the arm with the eyes as the arm(s) moves up, down and to the side.

Fig. 14

SAFETY CONSIDERATIONS: When adding head movements, such as looking up or down, begin with small range of motion and progress to greater range of motion. Do not exceed a range of motion where "centered" position cannot be maintained. When visually tracking an arm moving overhead, be especially aware of correct lumbar spinal alignment. Do not lean back or excessively arch the lower back. Attempt to maintain level foot positioning on the dome. Avoid excessive dorsi flexion, plantar flexion, inversion or eversion. The knees should be "soft" or flexed slightly, rather than locked in a hyper-extended position.

VARIATIONS AND COMMENTS: For more balance challenge, use arm movement patterns that track overhead and behind the body. Follow the arm movement with the head and eyes, while attempting to maintain "centered" position with the rest of the body (See Fig. 15).

Fig. 15

Balance, core stabilization and other exercises that challenge the vestibular system can be performed during the warm-up, or may be used as a recovery task between cardio drills or strength exercises.

EXERCISE GOAL: The goal of these exercises is to practice dynamic balance while performing a variety of rhythmic movement patterns. These movement patterns will challenge core stabilization, as well as hip, leg and ankle stabilization.

SETUP AND ALIGNMENT: Stand on top of the dome in "centered" position. Let the arms hang naturally at the sides of the body.

PERFORMING THE EXERCISE: Slowly begin to shift the weight from one foot to the other. Gradually increase the cadence of these weight shifts or alternating compressions. Allow the arms to pump forward and back in opposition to the feet (See Fig. 16). As balance and control improve, increase range of motion by lifting one heel. These compressions can progress to a walk, march or jog on top of the dome. Decrease range of motion and return to "centered" position. With the weight equally distributed between the feet, begin a double leg compression or bounce (See Fig. 17). Alternate the compressions and bouncing to practice the transition between unilateral and bilateral movements.

SAFETY CONSIDERATIONS: Dynamic, rhythmic movements may take more time to master than static balance exercises. Progress slowly, increasing cadence and range of motion as stabilizing strength, balance and skill level improves. While performing alternating compressions or jogging, maintain neutral spinal alignment, and avoid tipping the shoulders and pelvis to either side while the weight is on one leg. Contracting the core musculature will enhance balance performance and spinal posture. When performing the double leg bounce, keep the feet level on top of the dome and the weight centered over the arches of the feet.

VARIATIONS AND COMMENTS: For more dynamic balance challenge, add a small jump to the bouncing movement. Alternate easy bounces with a single jump (See Fig. 18). Land each jump with good alignment and control. After the alternating bounce/jump is mastered, perform a series of controlled jumps without any bouncing between each jump. Attempt to keep the upper body and trunk "quiet" during the jumps in order to maintain a stabilized, upright posture while performing dynamic extension of the hips and knees.

Fig. 16

Fig. 17

Fig. 18

BALANCE &
STABILIZATION EXERCISES

STANDING BALANCE

EXERCISE GOAL: The goal of these exercises is to challenge standing static balance, core stabilization, foot and ankle stabilization, and balance related to the vestibular system.

SETUP AND ALIGNMENT: Stand on top of the dome in "centered" position. Place one foot in the middle of the dome and shift all the weight onto this foot. The arms may be extended out to the sides at about waist height for balance assistance, or the hands may rest on the hips for more balance challenge.

PERFORMING THE EXERCISE: With the weight bearing leg centered on the top of the dome, place the inside of the other foot against the side of the dome. Keep the toes or inner foot against the dome for balance assistance, and adjust posture and spinal alignment. Lift the foot away from the dome slightly to test balance and stabilization. Hold this balanced position for 10 to 60 seconds (See Fig. 19). Slowly, lift the leg to a higher position and hold (See Fig. 20).

Fig. 19

Fig. 20

Then lower the leg onto the top of the dome, shift the weight onto the other foot and repeat the balance on the other side.

SAFETY CONSIDERATIONS: Attempt to maintain level foot positioning when standing on the dome. Avoid excessive dorsi flexion, plantar flexion, inversion or eversion. The knee of the weight bearing leg should be "soft" or flexed slightly, rather than locked in a hyperextended position. Maintain neutral spinal alignment, and avoid tipping the shoulders and pelvis to either side while the weight is on one leg. Contracting the core musculature will enhance balance performance.

VARIATIONS AND COMMENTS: For more balance and stabilization challenge, move the non-weight-bearing leg through different planes of motion. Lift the leg in front of the body, then circle to the side and behind the body. This drill can be performed with a bent or straight leg. For added vestibular challenge, turn or tilt the head from side to side while holding balance in any position. Closing the eyes while balancing on one leg is a very advanced challenge.

Any of the static or dynamic balance exercises detailed in the Warm-Up and Acclimation section are also effective as standing balance drills. Vestibular challenges such as turning or tilting the head, tracking hand movement or closing the eyes can be used with any single or double leg standing balance drill.

EXERCISE GOAL: The goal of these exercises is to challenge kneeling static balance, core stabilization, and hip stabilization.

SETUP AND ALIGNMENT: Kneel with the knees and lower legs (shins) centered on the top of the dome. For balance assistance, the toes may touch the floor. For more balance challenge, lift the toes off the floor. Place the arms out to the sides at about waist height for balance assistance, or the hands on the hips for more balance challenge. Align the body in "centered" position from the knees through the top of the head (See Fig. 21).

PERFORMING THE EXERCISE: Shift the weight onto one leg and slowly abduct the other leg slightly off the dome (See Fig. 22). For further balance challenge, abduct the leg to the highest point where proper alignment ("centered" position) can be maintained with the spine, shoulders and pelvis. Hold and balance for 10 to 60 seconds.

SAFETY CONSIDERATIONS: Maintain neutral spinal alignment in both the lumbar and cervical spine, and avoid tipping the shoulders and pelvis to either side while the weight is on one leg. Contracting the core musculature will enhance balance performance. Centering the front of the lower leg across the top of the dome will help avoid unnecessary pressure on the kneecap.

VARIATIONS AND COMMENTS: For more balance and stabilization challenge, move the non-weight-bearing leg through different planes of motion. Lift the leg in front of the body (See Fig. 23), then, circle to the side and behind the body. This drill can also be performed with a straight leg for more balance and flexibility challenge. As balance is mastered, point the toes of the back foot and attempt to keep them off the floor.

While performing static balances, such as a single knee balance, the body should be "quiet" but dynamic. Avoid any movement that is not necessary to maintain or correct balance. As skill level improves and stabilizing muscles strengthen, the body will use less and less movement to maintain the balance.

Fig. 21 *Fig. 22*

Fig. 23

Then, lower the leg down to the top of the dome, shift the weight onto the other knee and shin, and repeat the balance on the other side.

EXERCISE GOAL: The goal of these exercises is to challenge kneeling dynamic balance, core stabilization, hip stabilization, and balance related to the vestibular system.

SETUP AND ALIGNMENT: Kneel with the knees and lower legs (shins) centered on the top of the dome. For balance assistance, the toes may touch the floor. For more balance challenge, lift the toes off the floor. Place the arms out to the sides at about waist height for balance assistance, or the hands on the hips for more balance challenge. Align the body in "centered" position from the knees through the top of the head.

PERFORMING THE EXERCISE: Slowly rotate the trunk and touch the hands to the outer thigh or one of the heels. Visually track the hand movement with the head (See Fig. 24). Allow the hips to flex slightly to facilitate trunk rotation. Return to "centered" position and alternate sides.

Fig. 24

SAFETY CONSIDERATIONS: Begin these drills without visual tracking in order to master the movement pattern. Then, when the movement pattern is familiar, add the vestibular challenges. Contracting the core musculature will enhance balance performance. Centering the front of the lower leg across the top of the dome will help avoid unnecessary pressure on the kneecap.

VARIATIONS AND COMMENTS: As balance is mastered, point the toes of the back foot and attempt to keep them off the floor. For additional balance challenge, flex the hips and lower the trunk, reaching diagonally across the body with one arm. Begin by touching the front of the dome with the hand. Then, progress to touching the floor in front of the dome. Visually track the hand movement with the head (See Fig. 25). Return to upright, "centered" position and repeat on the other side. For a challenging drill, combine these two exercises with visual tracking to the back and diagonal tracking to the front.

Fig. 25

EXERCISE GOAL: The goal of these exercises is to challenge supine balance, core stabilization, and hip and shoulder girdle stabilization.

SETUP AND ALIGNMENT: Lie supine with the lumbar spine centered on the dome. Lift the legs until the knees are bent 90 degrees and aligned over the hips. Flex the elbows, holding the hands in a "ready" position (See Fig. 26). Hold this position until the body feels balanced and stable on the dome.

Fig. 26

PERFORMING THE EXERCISE: Slowly extend one leg until it is parallel to the floor or slightly higher. Flex the opposite shoulder until the biceps is near the ear and the arm is reaching overhead. Lower the other arm, extending the elbow, so that the arm is in line with the leg (See Fig. 27). Hold this position and balance for 10 to 60 seconds. Then, slowly reverse the movements and balance with the opposite leg and arm parallel to the floor for an equal amount of time.

Fig. 27

SAFETY CONSIDERATIONS: Keep the cervical spine aligned throughout the balance. Avoid flexing or hyperextending the neck. Begin the opposition arm/leg movement with a small range of motion, and gradually progress to the fully extended leg and arm. If the body tips in either direction (toward the head or feet), the positioning of the lumbar spine on the dome may need to be adjusted forward or back slightly.

VARIATIONS AND COMMENTS: For more balance and stabilization challenge, extend both legs out parallel to the floor, and both arms overhead in a position that is close to parallel to the floor (See Fig. 28). Do not allow the lumbar spine to release or arch off the dome while holding this challenging balance. Focus on core stabilization and scapular retraction while balancing.

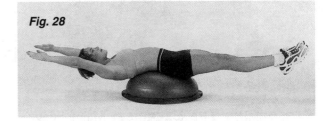

Fig. 28

EXERCISE GOAL: The goal of these exercises is to challenge supine balance, core stabilization, hip and shoulder girdle stabilization, and hip flexor flexibility.

SETUP AND ALIGNMENT: Sit on the floor and rest the upper back against the side of the dome. Center the thoracic spine, shoulders and neck on the top of the dome and slowly lift the hips until the upper thighs are parallel to the floor. Adjust the feet until they are approximately hip width apart, with the heels aligned under the knees. Place the hands on the floor for balance assistance, or on the hips for more balance challenge (See Fig. 29).

Fig. 29

PERFORMING THE EXERCISE: Maintaining tension (contractions) in the hamstrings, gluteal, and lumbar spinal extensor muscle groups, slowly flex the shoulders until the fingertips are reaching toward the ceiling. Retract the scapulae and hold this position for 10 to 60 seconds (See Fig. 30). For more balance challenge move the feet, knees and thighs closer together.

Fig. 30

SAFETY CONSIDERATIONS: Adjust the positioning of the upper back so that the neck is in a neutral position on top of the dome. If the shoulders are positioned too far forward on the dome, the cervical spine will be forced into flexion. If they are positioned too far back, the head will drop back and force the cervical spine into excessive hyperextension. Either full or partial scapular retraction may be executed during this exercise.

VARIATIONS AND COMMENTS: For more balance and stabilization challenge, slowly extend one knee until the leg is straight and about parallel with the floor (See Fig. 31). Hold this position for 10 to 60 seconds. Then, lower the foot to the floor, extend the other knee and balance on the other side. Placing the feet hip width apart will be more stable, while moving the feet together will add challenge.

Fig. 31

EXERCISE GOAL: The goal of these exercises is to challenge prone balance, core stabilization, and hip and shoulder girdle stabilization.

SETUP AND ALIGNMENT: Lie prone with the hips and abdomen centered on the dome. Place the hands on the floor in front of the platform. Keeping the cervical, thoracic and lumbar spine aligned in neutral posture, slowly lift the legs until they are parallel to the floor (See Fig. 32).

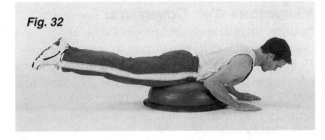
Fig. 32

PERFORMING THE EXERCISE: Slowly lift one arm off the floor, flexing the shoulder until the arm is reaching overhead. When balance and stabilization are established, lift the other arm into the same position. Adjust hip and shoulder girdle positioning until the arms and legs are parallel to the floor (See Fig. 33). Hold this position and balance for 10 to 60 seconds. To add proprioceptive challenge, bend one knee, reach behind the body with the opposite arm, and grasp the foot with the hand. The opposite arm and leg remain extended and parallel to the floor (See Fig. 34). Hold this position, then release and

perform the balance with the opposite arm and leg. For a dynamic exercise, slowly alternate from side to side with just a slight pause after grasping or touching the foot.

SAFETY CONSIDERATIONS: Limb length and body mass will affect body positioning and balance on the dome. If the body tips in either direction (toward the head or feet), the positioning of the hips and abdomen on the dome may need to be adjusted forward or back slightly. Do not lift the head and hyperextend the cervical spine. To modify this prone balance, let the toes of one foot rest on the floor throughout the exercise, and place the arms out to the sides ("airplane" position) rather than overhead.

VARIATIONS AND COMMENTS: For more balance, stabilization and proprioceptive challenge, add a "seesaw" movement to the fully extended prone balance. Extend the hips slightly, allowing the body to tilt forward in an aligned position. The fingers should lightly touch or be slightly above the floor (See Fig. 35). Then extend the lumbar spine slightly so that the body tilts back. The toes should lightly touch or be slightly above the floor. This variation may also be performed with the arms out to the sides in "airplane" position. Hold and balance for a few seconds in each position.

Fig. 35

Fig. 33

Fig. 34

EXERCISE GOAL: The goal of these exercises is to challenge prone dynamic balance, core stabilization, and hip and shoulder girdle stabilization.

SETUP AND ALIGNMENT: Lie prone with the hips and abdomen centered on the dome. Place the hands or elbows on the floor in front of the platform. Keeping the cervical, thoracic and lumbar spine aligned in neutral posture, slowly lift the legs until they are parallel to the floor.

PERFORMING THE EXERCISE: Holding this aligned position, slowly begin to flutter the legs (See Fig. 36). When balance and stabilization in the trunk and hips are established, flex the shoulders until the arms are overhead and parallel to the floor. Simultaneously flutter the arms and legs (See Fig. 37). Hold this balance and flutter the arms and legs for 10 to 60 seconds.

SAFETY CONSIDERATIONS: Initiate the flutter movement from the hips and shoulders, rather than from the knees and elbows. Keep the arms and legs parallel to the floor. Limb length and body mass will affect body positioning and balance on the dome. If the body tips in either direction (toward the head or feet), the positioning of the hips and abdomen on the dome may need to be adjusted forward or back slightly. Do not lift the head and hyperextend the cervical spine.

VARIATIONS AND COMMENTS: For more balance, stabilization and proprioceptive challenge, add a slight roll side to side while fluttering the legs and arms. Roll from the front of one hip to the other, allowing the shoulders to roll slightly with the hips (See Fig. 38). Keep the arms and legs parallel to the floor while rolling side to side.

Fig. 38

Fig. 36

Fig. 37

EXERCISE GOAL: The goal of these exercises is to challenge prone balance, core stabilization, and hip and shoulder girdle stabilization.

SETUP AND ALIGNMENT: Kneel with the hands on the floor and the knees centered on top of the dome. Align the wrists under the shoulders, with the hands about shoulder width apart. Lift one leg, extending the hip until the leg is approximately parallel to the floor (See Fig. 39). For balance assistance, the toes of the supporting leg may touch the floor. For more balance challenge, lift the toes off the floor.

Fig. 39

PERFORMING THE EXERCISE: Slowly lift the arm that is opposite the extended leg until it is parallel to the floor and aligned with the shoulder (See Fig. 40). Hold this position for 10 to 60 seconds. Then, lower the arm and leg and repeat on the other side. This exercise can be performed as a static balance, or the arm and leg may be lifted and lowered, slowly and repeatedly, for a dynamic balance challenge.

Fig. 40

SAFETY CONSIDERATIONS: Maintain neutral posture in the lumbar and cervical spine. The gaze should be down toward the floor, slightly ahead of the supporting hand. Avoid lifting the head and hyperextending the neck. Keep the shoulders and hips level throughout the exercise. Do not "open" the hip or the shoulder while lifting the arm and leg. Firmly contract the abdominal muscle group for enhanced core stabilization.

VARIATIONS AND COMMENTS: To add proprioceptive challenge, bend the knee of the extended leg, reach behind the body with the opposite arm, and grasp the foot with the hand (See Fig. 41). Hold this position, then release and perform the balance with the opposite arm and leg.

For a dynamic balance challenge, simultaneously pull the elbow and knee of the extended arm and leg in toward the core. Allow the lumbar spine to flex slightly. Then, return the arm and leg to the starting position, and the lumbar spine to neutral.

Fig. 41

EXERCISE GOAL: The goal of these exercises is to challenge prone dynamic balance, core stabilization, hip, shoulder and shoulder girdle stabilization, and balance related to the vestibular system.

SETUP AND ALIGNMENT: Kneel on the floor on a mat or other padded surface. Turn the BOSU to a "platform side up" position. Grasp the handles on the sides of the platform. Adjust body positioning so that the chest and shoulders are aligned over the center of the platform, and the trunk forms a straight line from the shoulders to the knees. Rest the toes on the floor.

PERFORMING THE EXERCISE: Slowly tilt the platform to one side, while keeping the elbows extended (See Fig. 42). Allow the hips and shoulders to tilt slightly with the platform. Return to centered position and tilt to the other side. To execute a variation requiring more strength, extend the legs fully and balance on the toes. Perform the same side-to-side tilt (See Fig. 43).

SAFETY CONSIDERATIONS: Keeping the elbows extended during the tilt allows the entire body to tilt and challenges core stability. Do not tilt the platform so far that the fingers can get pinched between the floor and the platform. Avoid shifting the weight back. Instead, preserve shoulder over wrist alignment at all times. Maintain neutral posture in the lumbar and cervical spine throughout the exercise. Partial scapular retraction will help stabilize the shoulder girdle while tilting and returning to center.

VARIATIONS AND COMMENTS: For more balance, stabilization and strength challenge, alternate leg lifts while tilting the platform. Extend the hip of the leg that is opposite to the direction of platform tilt (See Fig. 44). For additional vestibular challenge, close the eyes while performing any of the variations.

Fig. 44

Fig. 42

Fig. 43

EXERCISE GOAL: The goal of these exercises is to challenge prone dynamic balance, core stabilization, hip, shoulder and shoulder girdle stabilization, and balance related to the vestibular system.

SETUP AND ALIGNMENT: Kneel on the floor on a mat or other padded surface. Turn the BOSU to a "platform side up" position. Grasp the handles on the sides of the platform. Adjust body positioning so that the chest and shoulders are aligned over the center of the platform, and the trunk forms a straight line from the shoulders to the knees. Rest the toes on the floor.

PERFORMING THE EXERCISE: Slowly tilt the platform forward, while keeping the elbows extended (See Fig. 45). Return to centered position and tilt the platform in the opposite direction. To execute a variation requiring more strength, extend the legs fully and balance on the toes. Perform the same forward and back tilt (See Fig. 46).

SAFETY CONSIDERATIONS: Keep the trunk stable while tilting the platform forward and back. Do not lift the trunk up and down, or shift the trunk forward or back, as the platform tilts. Instead, move from the shoulder joint to execute the tilts. Keep the elbows extended during the tilt. Maintain neutral posture in the lumbar and cervical spine throughout the exercise. Partial scapular retraction will help stabilize the shoulder girdle while tilting and returning to center.

VARIATIONS AND COMMENTS: For more balance, stabilization and strength challenge, alternate leg lifts while tilting the platform. Extend either leg as the platform is tilted (See Fig. 47). For additional vestibular challenge, close the eyes while performing any of the variations.

Fig. 47

Fig. 45

Fig. 46

EXERCISE GOAL: The goal of these exercises is to challenge supine balance, core stabilization, pelvis and shoulder girdle stabilization.

SETUP AND ALIGNMENT: Sit with the hips centered directly on top of the dome. Place the hands on the sides of the dome for balance assistance. Lean back slightly, maintaining neutral posture in the lumbar spine. Flexing the knee, lift one leg to a point where the lower leg is about parallel to the floor (See Fig. 48).

Fig. 48

PERFORMING THE EXERCISE: Slowly lift the second leg to the same height as the first. Keep the hands on the dome for balance assistance, or lift the arms and reach toward the toes for more balance challenge (See Fig. 49). Hold this bent knee, v-sit position for 10 to 60 seconds, attempting to keep the lower legs parallel to the floor. Then, lower one leg at a time back to the floor, and return to an upright, seated position.

Fig. 49

SAFETY CONSIDERATIONS: Keep the back "straight" throughout all v-sit variations. Avoid flexing the lumbar spine, instead attempt to maintain a neutral lumbar curve. A slight anterior pelvic tilt will help maintain correct pelvic and lumbar alignment. If the spine flexes, due to lack of flexibility or lack of strength in the lumbar spinal extensor muscle group, lift one leg at a time (instead of both legs) while focusing on correct lumbar positioning. Maintain neutral cervical alignment. Partial scapular retraction will stabilize the shoulder girdle while leaning back and balancing.

VARIATIONS AND COMMENTS: For a modified progression, lift one leg at a time, alternating sides. When correct lumbar positioning can be maintained, lift both legs and rest the heels on the dome. Practice balancing here, then lift the heels off the dome.

For additional balance, stabilization and flexibility challenges, extend both legs (See Fig. 50). Reach past the knees with the fingertips.

Fig. 50

EXERCISE GOAL: The goal of these exercises is to challenge sidelying balance, core stabilization, hip, pelvis, adductor and shoulder girdle stabilization.

SETUP AND ALIGNMENT: In a sidelying position, center the waist directly on top of the dome. Rest the elbow and lower arm on the floor. Place the other hand on the hip. Lift both legs until they are parallel to the floor (See Fig. 51).

Fig. 51

PERFORMING THE EXERCISE: Stabilize the body and balance in this supported position. Then, slowly lift the bottom arm off the floor and cross the arms over the chest. Align the trunk and legs so that they are parallel to the floor (See Fig. 52). Hold this position and balance for 10 to 60 seconds. Then, release and perform the balance on the other side.

Fig. 52

SAFETY CONSIDERATIONS: Keep the shoulders and hips aligned over one another. Do not let the top hip or shoulder roll forward or back. Limb length and body mass will affect body positioning and balance on the dome. If the body tips in either direction (toward the head or feet), the positioning of the hips and waist on the dome may need to be adjusted forward or back slightly. Attempt to maintain neutral lumbar and cervical alignment. Isometric adduction of the legs will help stabilize the pelvis, while partial scapular retraction will help stabilize the shoulder girdle.

VARIATIONS AND COMMENTS: For more balance and stabilization challenge, reach overhead with both arms and hold the balance. Attempt to maintain a position where the arms, trunk and legs are parallel to the floor (See Fig. 53). Repeat the balance on the other side.

Fig. 53

EXERCISE GOAL: The goal of these exercises is to challenge dynamic sidelying balance, core stabilization, and hip, pelvis and shoulder girdle stabilization.

SETUP AND ALIGNMENT: In a sidelying position, center the waist directly on top of the dome. Rest the elbow and lower arm on the floor. Extend the other arm overhead. Lift the top leg until it is parallel to the floor (See Fig. 54).

Fig. 54

PERFORMING THE EXERCISE: Practice the dynamic movement by pulling the elbow and knee of the upper arm and leg into toward the core (See Fig. 55). When this movement is coordinated and balanced, progress to pulling both knees and the top elbow into the core (See Fig. 56). Pause for a few seconds at the peak of

Fig. 55

Fig. 56

the movement, then return to the starting position. Repeat the tuck multiple times for a dynamic balance challenge. Then, release and perform the balance on the other side.

SAFETY CONSIDERATIONS: In the tuck position, the lumbar spine is flexed. The trunk and upper body must rotate slightly to the back when pulling in both the legs and arms. This will help counterbalance the weight of the legs and prevent the body from tipping forward off the dome. Return to neutral spinal position when releasing from the tuck.

VARIATIONS AND COMMENTS: For additional balance and stabilization challenge, simultaneously pull both arms and both legs in toward the core (See Fig. 57). Pause for a few seconds at the peak of the movement, then return to the starting position. To add a very advanced challenge, do not rest the arm and leg down on the floor after each tuck. Instead, simultaneously extend the arms and legs to a sidelying balance position that is parallel to the floor. Repeat the variation on the other side.

Fig. 57

MUSCULAR STRENGTH, ENDURANCE & STABILIZATION EXERCISES

• • • • •

SUPINE TRUNK CURL

EXERCISE GOAL: The goal of these exercises is to challenge muscular endurance and strength in the rectus abdominis, and internal/external obliques, as well as supine balance, core stabilization and shoulder girdle stabilization.

SETUP AND ALIGNMENT: Lie in a supine incline position with the thoracic spine centered on the dome. Position the feet flat on the floor, about shoulder width apart. Allow the hips to rest against the side of the dome near the platform. Partially retract the scapulae. Then, with the neck in neutral posture, interlace the fingers behind the head for more cervical support, or place the fists at the temples with elbows open for more cervical stabilization challenge (See Fig. 58).

Fig. 58

PERFORMING THE EXERCISE: Slowly flex the trunk, pulling the bottom of the ribcage down toward the top of the hip bones (See Fig. 59). Pause at the top of the movement, then slowly lower back to the starting position. Repeat for the appropriate number of repetitions.

Fig. 59

SAFETY CONSIDERATIONS: Begin with the lumbar spine in a neutral or slightly extended position, and return to this position after each curl. Do not completely release or "collapse"

during the eccentric, or lowering, phase of the curl. Attempt to maintain neutral cervical posture, avoiding excessive neck flexion during the curl. Maintain partial scapular retraction throughout the curl. This will stabilize the shoulder girdle and help prevent scapular protraction and shoulder joint movement. By limiting this extra motion (or momentum into the movement), the abdominal muscle groups will be more effectively isolated and challenged.

VARIATIONS AND COMMENTS: For more challenge, lie supine with the lumbar spine centered on the dome. Begin in a position where the trunk is parallel to the floor or slightly extended over the dome (See Fig. 60). Slowly flex the trunk, pulling the bottom of the ribcage down toward the top of the hip bones (See Fig. 61). Pause at the top of the movement, then slowly lower back to the starting position. In either of the starting positions, trunk flexion with rotation may also be performed. Initiate the motion with trunk flexion, then smoothly merge into trunk rotation. The obliques, which flex, laterally flex and rotate the trunk are challenged in a different way with this variation, when compared to isolated trunk flexion. For more balance and stabilization challenge with any variation, move the feet to a narrow stance where the insides of the feet, knees and thighs are lightly touching.

Fig. 60

Fig. 61

EXERCISE GOAL: The goal of these exercises is to challenge muscular endurance and strength in the rectus abdominis, and internal/external obliques, as well as supine balance, core stabilization and shoulder girdle stabilization.

SETUP AND ALIGNMENT: Lie in a supine position with the lumbar spine centered on the dome. Lift the legs until the knees are bent 90 degrees and aligned over the hips. Partially retract the scapulae. Then, with the neck in neutral posture, interlace the fingers behind the head for more cervical support, or place the fists at the temples with elbows open for more cervical stabilization challenge (See Fig. 62).

Fig. 62

PERFORMING THE EXERCISE: Extend the lumbar spine slightly by tilting the pelvis in an anterior direction. Then, slowly flex the trunk, pulling the bottom of the ribcage down toward the top of the hip bones. Simultaneously perform a posterior pelvic tilt, pulling the top of the hip bones up toward the ribs (See Fig. 63). Pause at the top of the movement, then slowly lower back to the starting position. Repeat for the appropriate number of repetitions.

Fig. 63

SAFETY CONSIDERATIONS: Return to the slightly extended spine/pelvis position after each curl and tilt. Do not completely release or "collapse" during the eccentric, or lowering, phase. Attempt to maintain neutral cervical posture, avoiding excessive neck flexion at the top of the curl. Maintain partial scapular retraction throughout the curl. This will stabilize the shoulder girdle and help prevent scapular protraction and shoulder joint movement. By limiting this extra motion (or momentum into the movement), the abdominal muscle groups will be more effectively isolated and challenged.

VARIATIONS AND COMMENTS: For a slightly different challenge, trunk flexion with rotation may be performed with the pelvic tilt. Initiate the motion with trunk flexion, then smoothly merge into trunk rotation. The obliques, which flex, laterally flex and rotate the trunk are challenged in a different way with this variation, when compared to isolated trunk flexion. Rotating the trunk while simultaneously tilting the pelvis will also create more balance and stabilization challenge.

EXERCISE GOAL: The goal of these exercises is to challenge muscular endurance and strength in the rectus abdominis, and internal/external obliques, as well as supine balance, core stabilization and shoulder girdle stabilization.

SETUP AND ALIGNMENT: Lie in a supine position with the lumbar spine centered on the dome. Lift the legs until the knees are bent 90 degrees and aligned over the hips. Flex the trunk slightly and hold the "curl" position. Place the hands in a "ready" position with the palms facing the knees. Hold this position until the body feels balanced and stable on the dome.

PERFORMING THE EXERCISE: Slowly begin to alternate the legs in a small "bicycle" motion. Flex and extend the elbows, following the leg movement with the arms (See Fig. 64). When this motion feels balanced and stable, place the fingertips at the temples with the elbows open, and begin to rotate the trunk from side to side. Then, increase the range of motion of the "bicycling" action of the legs by pulling one knee in toward the chest while simultaneously extending the other parallel to the floor. The trunk should rotate toward the knee that is being pulled upward (See Fig. 65). Repeat for the appropriate number of repetitions.

SAFETY CONSIDERATIONS: Rotate the trunk, rather than crossing the elbows over the midline of the body. Partial scapular retraction will stabilize the shoulder girdle and help isolate the core musculature. Attempt to maintain neutral cervical posture throughout the exercise. When progressing from the small range of motion to greater range of motion "bicycle," lumbar positioning on the dome may need to be adjusted. If the body is tilting down in the direction of the legs, adjust the hips slightly higher on the dome until balance is established in this longer lever and extended position.

VARIATIONS AND COMMENTS: For more balance and stabilization challenge, stabilize the trunk in neutral posture and perform the full range of motion "bicycle" motion with the legs, but do not rotate the trunk. Instead, reach overhead with the arm that is opposite the extended leg, and reach down the leg with the arm on the same side as the extended leg. Scissor the arms through long lever shoulder flexion as the legs "bicycle." For a slightly different challenge, reach overhead with the arm that is on the same side as the extended leg, and touch the knee with the opposite arm (See Fig. 66). The extended arm and leg can be lifted at a 45 degree angle from the floor, or extend to a position that is parallel to the floor for more challenge.

Fig. 64

Fig. 65

Fig. 66

EXERCISE GOAL: The goal of these exercises is to challenge muscular endurance and strength in the rectus abdominis, and internal/external obliques, as well as supine balance, core stabilization, hip and shoulder girdle stabilization.

SETUP AND ALIGNMENT: Lie in a supine position with the lumbar spine centered on the dome. Lift one leg until the knee is bent 90 degrees and aligned over the hips. Partially retract the scapulae. Then, with the neck in neutral posture, interlace the fingers behind the head for more cervical support, or place the fists at the temples with elbows open for more cervical stabilization challenge. Flex the trunk slightly and hold this "curl" position (See Fig. 67).

Fig. 67

PERFORMING THE EXERCISE: Slowly rotate the trunk in the direction away from the lifted leg. Rotate until the back elbow is close to the floor and aligned with the midline of the trunk (See Fig. 68). Hold this position for a few seconds, then slowly rotate back to the starting position. Rotate the trunk in the opposite direction (toward the lifted leg), directing the back elbow toward the floor. Hold this position for a few seconds, then slowly return to the starting position. Change legs, and repeat the trunk rotation sequence with the opposite leg lifted.

Fig. 68

SAFETY CONSIDERATIONS: Rotate, using the trunk muscles, keeping the elbows in alignment with the shoulders. Maintain partial scapular retraction to help stabilize the shoulder girdle region and avoid rounding of the upper back during trunk rotation. Attempt to maintain level hip alignment. Avoid tipping the hips to either side while rotating the trunk.

VARIATIONS AND COMMENTS: For more balance and proprioceptive challenge, let the head and eyes follow the elbow as it reaches for the floor (See Fig. 69). In addition, extend the knee of the leg that is lifted off the floor. Repeat the trunk rotation movement in both directions, maintaining the extended leg position. Then, change legs and repeat the exercise sequence.

Fig. 69

EXERCISE GOAL: The goal of these exercises is to challenge muscular endurance and strength in the rectus abdominis and internal/external obliques, as well as supine balance, core stabilization, and pelvic and shoulder girdle stabilization.

SETUP AND ALIGNMENT: Sit with the hips centered directly on top of the dome. Flex the knees approximately 90 degrees and rest the toes lightly on the floor. Place the hands on the sides of the dome for balance assistance. Lean back slightly, maintaining neutral posture in the lumbar spine.

PERFORMING THE EXERCISE: Slowly tilt the legs from side to side, maintaining neutral spinal posture. Allow the torso to counter rotate in the opposite direction that the legs are moving (See Fig. 70). The head and gaze should move in the same direction that the torso is rotating. When correct lumbar positioning can be maintained, flex one knee and lift the leg to a point where the lower leg is about parallel to the floor. In this "half v-sit" position, continue to move the legs to one side and rotate the torso to the opposite side.

Fig. 70

Keep the hands on the dome for balance assistance, or clasp the hands at about chest height for more balance challenge (See Fig. 71). Repeat for the appropriate number of repetitions.

Fig. 71

SAFETY CONSIDERATIONS: Keep the back "straight" throughout all v-sit variations. Avoid flexing the lumbar spine. Instead, attempt to maintain a neutral lumbar curve. A slight anterior pelvic tilt will help maintain correct pelvic and lumbar alignment. If the spine flexes, due to lack of flexibility or lack of strength in the lumbar spinal extensor muscle group, keep one leg or both legs on the floor while focusing on correct lumbar positioning. Maintain neutral cervical alignment. Partial scapular retraction will stabilize the shoulder girdle while leaning back and balancing.

VARIATIONS AND COMMENTS: For more balance and stabilization challenge, lift both legs until the lower legs are about parallel to the floor. Keeping the thighs close together, move the legs to one side and counter rotate the torso and arms (See Fig. 72).

Fig. 72

EXERCISE GOAL: The goal of these exercises is to enhance pelvic mobility, challenge core stabilization and seated balance, and practice moving in and out of neutral lumbar posture.

SETUP AND ALIGNMENT: Sit with the hips centered directly on top of the dome. Flex the knees approximately 90 degrees and place the feet flat on the floor, about hip width apart. Adjust the distance of the heels from the platform in order to maintain upright, neutral spinal posture. Rest the hands lightly on the knees or lower legs (See Fig. 73).

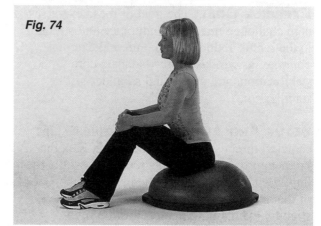

Fig. 74

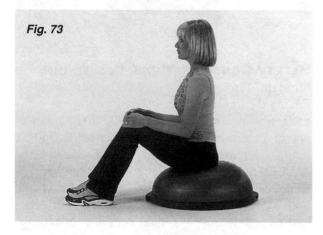

Fig. 73

Fig. 75

PERFORMING THE EXERCISE: Maintaining upright posture, tilt the hips in an anterior direction (See Fig. 74). Hold this position for a few seconds. Then, return to neutral lumbar posture. From the neutral position, tilt the hips in a posterior direction (See Fig. 75). Hold this position for a few seconds. Then, return to the starting position. Repeat for the appropriate number of repetitions.

SAFETY CONSIDERATIONS: Maintain neutral cervical posture while tilting the pelvis in either direction. Partial scapular retraction will stabilize the shoulder girdle and help isolate the movement in the pelvic region and lumbar spine.

VARIATIONS AND COMMENTS: Anterior and posterior tilts can help improve pelvic mobility, as well as help to strengthen the abdominal muscle groups and lumbar spinal extensors.

EXERCISE GOAL: The goal of these exercises is to challenge muscular endurance and strength in the rectus abdominis, internal/external obliques, quadratus lumborum and spinal extensor group, as well as sidelying balance, core stabilization, hip, pelvis, adductor/abductor and shoulder girdle stabilization.

Fig. 77

SETUP AND ALIGNMENT: In a sidelying position, center the waist directly on top of the dome. Adjust the legs into a long lever, "scissor" position with the top leg forward of the bottom leg. Place the hands behind the head. Point the top elbow toward the ceiling and the bottom elbow forward. Allow the trunk to laterally flex toward the floor, until a slight stretch is felt down the side of the torso (See Fig. 76).

Fig. 78

Fig. 76

PERFORMING THE EXERCISE: Laterally flex the trunk, pulling the bottom side of the ribcage down toward the top of the hip bone (See Fig. 77). Pause at the top of the movement, then slowly lower back to the starting position. When this variation feels balanced and stable, move the legs from a "scissored" stance to a position where the ankles and knees are aligned directly on top of each other. Laterally flex (See Fig. 78), then lower back to a lateral stretch. Repeat on both sides for the appropriate number of repetitions.

SAFETY CONSIDERATIONS: Initiate the lateral flexion movement with the trunk musculature, rather than by laterally flexing the neck. Maintain neutral alignment of the cervical spine throughout the exercise. Keep the hips and shoulders aligned over one another. Do not allow the hips and shoulders to tip forward or back.

VARIATIONS AND COMMENTS: For more balance and stabilization challenge, abduct the top leg while simultaneously laterally flexing the trunk. Pause at the top of the movement and hold the balance (See Fig. 79). Then, slowly lower back to the starting position. Repeat on both sides for the appropriate number of repetitions.

Fig. 79

EXERCISE GOAL: The goal of these exercises is to challenge muscular endurance and strength in the lumbar spinal extensors, as well as prone balance, core stabilization, and shoulder girdle stabilization.

Fig. 81

SETUP AND ALIGNMENT: Lie prone with the hips and abdomen centered on the dome. Passively flex the trunk, draping over the dome with the head, knees and toes resting lightly on the floor. Place the hands on the sides of the hips or upper thighs (See Fig. 80).

Fig. 82

Fig. 80

PERFORMING THE EXERCISE: Slowly extend the spine, moving through neutral position and into a range of comfortable spinal extension. Pause at the top of the movement (See Fig. 81). Then, slowly lower back to the starting position. For more overload, place the hands behind the head or under the forehead with the elbows open to the sides. Extend the spine to a proper range (See Fig. 82). Then lower back to the starting position. Repeat for the appropriate number of repetitions.

SAFETY CONSIDERATIONS: Initiate the movement with the lumbar spinal extensors, rather than by lifting the head. Maintain neutral cervical alignment throughout the exercise. Partial scapular retraction will stabilize the shoulder girdle and help isolate the movement in the lumbar region. Extend and flex the spine at a slow, even tempo. Avoid using momentum or ballistic movement to extend the spine, and keep the motion smooth.

VARIATIONS AND COMMENTS: For more balance and stabilization challenge, flex the shoulders until both arms are overhead and placed about shoulder width apart. Retract and depress the scapulae. Extend and flex the spine, as performed previously, holding the arms in this position (See Fig. 83).

Fig. 83

EXERCISE GOAL: The goal of these exercises is to challenge muscular endurance and strength in the lumbar spinal extensors and deep lumbar rotators, as well as prone balance, core stabilization, and shoulder girdle stabilization.

SETUP AND ALIGNMENT: Lie prone with the hips and abdomen centered on the dome. Passively flex the trunk, draping over the dome with the head, knees and toes resting lightly on the floor. Place the hands on the sides of the hips or upper thighs (See Fig. 84).

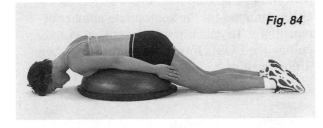

Fig. 84

PERFORMING THE EXERCISE: Begin to slowly extend the spine. Then, continue the extension while simultaneously rotating the trunk to one side. Pause at the top of the movement (See Fig. 85). Slowly lower back to the starting position. Repeat multiple repetitions on one side, or alternate sides. For more overload, place the hands behind the head, under the forehead, or at the temples with the elbows open to the sides. Extend and rotate the spine to a proper range (See Fig. 86). Lower back to the starting position. Repeat on both sides for the appropriate number of repetitions.

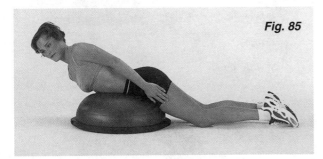

Fig. 85

Fig. 86

SAFETY CONSIDERATIONS: Initiate the extension/rotation movement at the lumbar spine, rather than by lifting the head. Maintain neutral cervical alignment throughout the exercise. Partial scapular retraction will stabilize the shoulder girdle and help isolate the movement in the lumbar region. Move with a slow, even tempo while both lifting and lowering the trunk. Avoid using momentum or ballistic movement to extend and rotate the spine, and keep the motion smooth.

VARIATIONS AND COMMENTS: For more balance and stabilization challenge, fully extend the legs, and balance with the toes touching the floor. Extend and rotate the spine while simultaneously lifting one leg. Lift the leg that is opposite to the direction of spinal rotation (See Fig. 87). Lower the trunk and leg simultaneously. Then, repeat on the other side. Alternate sides for the appropriate number of repetitions.

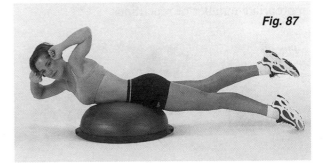

Fig. 87

EXERCISE GOAL: The goal of these exercises is to challenge muscular endurance and strength in the rectus abdominis, internal/external obliques, and hip flexor group, as well as prone balance, core stabilization, hip and pelvic stabilization, and shoulder girdle/shoulder joint stabilization.

SETUP AND ALIGNMENT: Lie prone with the lower thighs, knees and shins centered on the dome. Flex the elbows and place the palms and lower arms on the floor. The shoulders should be aligned over the elbows. Align the body in this "low-plank" position so that the lumbar spine is in neutral posture (See Fig. 88). The weight should be equally distributed between the upper and lower body.

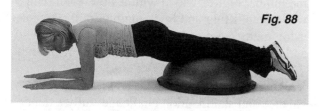

Fig. 88

PERFORMING THE EXERCISE: Contracting the abdominal muscle groups, slowly flex at the hips and "pike" up a few degrees. Press the front of the legs down into the dome and attempt to pull the BOSU forward during the pike up (See Fig. 89). Pause at the top of the movement. Then, slowly lower back to the starting position. Repeat for the appropriate number of repetitions.

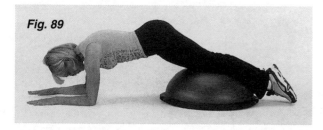

Fig. 89

SAFETY CONSIDERATIONS: Maintain neutral lumbar and cervical spinal posture throughout the exercise. Avoid flexing or rounding the lumbar spine. Do not lift the head or "collapse" in the lower back. Partial scapular retraction and scapular depression will help stabilize the shoulder girdle. The more advanced progressions of this exercise may not be appropriate for those with orthopedic concerns associated with the wrist or shoulder.

VARIATIONS AND COMMENTS: For more strength, balance and stabilization challenge, center the feet and ankles on the dome. Extend the elbows and place the palms on the floor, aligned under the shoulders. Align the body in this "high-plank" position so that the lumbar spine is in neutral posture (See Fig. 90). Pike up until approximately 90 degrees of hip flexion is achieved (See Fig. 91). Pause at the top of the movement. Then, lower back to the starting position. To further challenge balance and stabilization, simultaneously lift one leg while performing a pike up (See Fig. 92). Repeat either variation for the appropriate number of repetitions. To enhance the movement, visualize pulling the BOSU forward with the toes while lifting the hips.

Fig. 90

Fig. 91

Fig. 92

Prone Platform Push-Ups – Shoulder Horizontal Adduction

Exercise Goal: The goal of these exercises is to challenge muscular endurance and strength in the pectoralis muscle group, anterior deltoids and triceps, as well as prone dynamic balance, core stabilization, hip, shoulder and shoulder girdle stabilization, and balance related to the vestibular system.

Setup And Alignment: Kneel on the floor, on a mat or other padded surface. Turn the BOSU to a "platform side up" position. Grasp the handles on the sides of the platform, keeping the arms fully extended. Adjust body positioning so that the chest and shoulders are aligned over the center of the platform. Rest the toes on the floor.

Performing The Exercise: Slowly flex the elbows, lowering the chest toward the center of the platform. Allow the elbows to open to the sides so that the shoulders move through horizontal abduction (See Fig. 93). Pause at the bottom of the movement. Then, slowly extend the elbows and press back up to the starting position (horizontal adduction). When a level platform can be maintained while performing the push-up in a bent-knee position, the knees may be fully extended. Perform the push-up as described previously, maintaining an aligned position from the ankles through the ears (See Fig. 94). Repeat for the appropriate number of repetitions.

Fig. 93

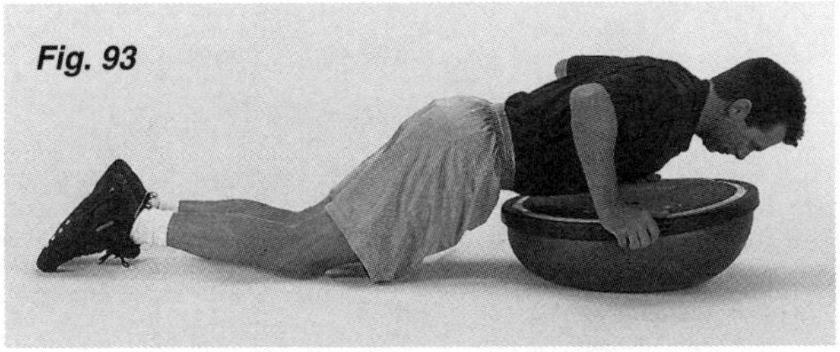

Fig. 94

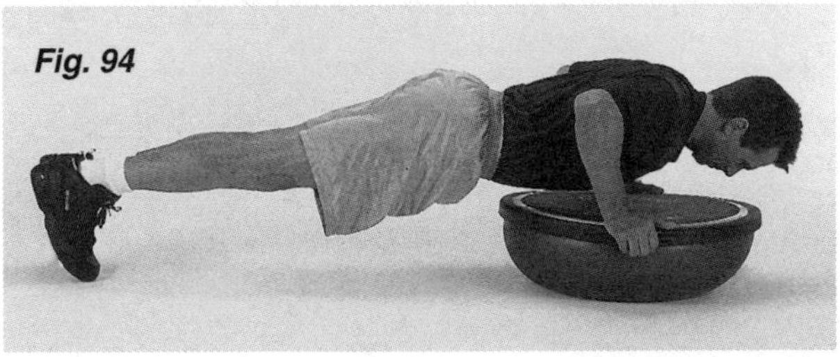

Safety Considerations: Keep the nipple line of the chest aligned over the center of the platform. Maintain neutral lumbar and cervical spinal posture throughout the exercise. Do not lift the head or "collapse" in the lower back. Partial scapular retraction and scapular depression will help stabilize the shoulder girdle. These exercises may not be appropriate for those with orthopedic concerns associated with the wrist or shoulder.

Variations And Comments: For more strength, balance and stabilization challenge, lift one leg while performing the extended knee push-up (See Fig. 95). Hold one leg up while performing multiple repetitions (alternate sides midway through the reps), or alternately lift a leg with each push-up. For more vestibular challenge, close the eyes with any variation.

Fig. 95

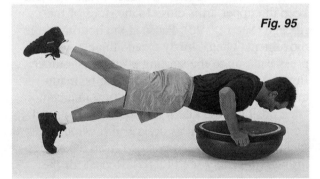

EXERCISE GOAL: The goal of these exercises is to challenge muscular endurance and strength in the pectoralis muscle group, triceps and anterior deltoids, as well as prone dynamic balance, core stabilization, hip, shoulder and shoulder girdle stabilization, and balance related to the vestibular system.

SETUP AND ALIGNMENT: Kneel on the floor on a mat or other padded surface. Turn the BOSU to a "platform side up" position. Grasp the handles on the sides of the platform, keeping the arms fully extended. Adjust body positioning so that the chest and shoulders are aligned over the center of the platform. Rest the toes on the floor.

PERFORMING THE EXERCISE: Slowly flex the elbows, lowering the chest toward the center of the platform. Point the elbows back, so that the shoulders move through shoulder extension, and keep the upper arms close to the sides of the ribcage (See Fig. 96). Pause at the bottom of the movement. Then, slowly extend the elbows and press back up to the starting position (shoulder flexion). When a level platform can be maintained while performing the push-up in a bent-knee position, the knees may be fully extended. Perform the push-up as described previously, maintaining an aligned position from the ankles through the ears (See Fig. 97). Repeat for the appropriate number of repetitions.

SAFETY CONSIDERATIONS: Keep the nipple line of the chest aligned over the center of the platform. Maintain neutral lumbar and cervical spinal posture throughout the exercise. Do not lift the head or "collapse" in the lower back. Partial scapular retraction and scapular depression will help stabilize the shoulder girdle. These exercises may not be appropriate for those with orthopedic concerns associated with the wrist or shoulder.

VARIATIONS AND COMMENTS: For more strength, balance and stabilization challenge, lift one leg while performing the extended knee push-up (See Fig. 98). Hold one leg up while performing multiple repetitions (alternate sides midway through the reps), or alternately lift a leg with each push-up. For more vestibular challenge, close the eyes with any variation.

Fig. 98

Fig. 96

Fig. 97

EXERCISE GOAL: The goal of these exercises is to challenge muscular endurance and strength in the trapezius (parts II, III and IV) and rhomboids, as well as seated dynamic balance, core stabilization, shoulder and shoulder girdle stabilization.

SETUP AND ALIGNMENT: Sit with the hips slightly forward of the top of the dome. Flex the knees and rest the feet flat on the floor, about hip width apart. Place the hands on the sides of the dome with the fingers facing down. Let the weight of the body sink into the dome, passively elevating the scapulae (See Fig. 99).

Fig. 99

PERFORMING THE EXERCISE: Slowly depress the scapulae, keeping the elbows straight. Let the hips lift slightly off the dome (See Fig. 100). Pause at the top of the movement. Then, slowly elevate the scapulae and lower back to the starting position. Repeat for the appropriate number of repetitions.

Fig. 100

SAFETY CONSIDERATIONS: Avoid using the legs to push the body up. Instead, stabilize the trunk and isolate the movement in the shoulder girdle region. Maintain neutral lumbar and cervical posture throughout the exercise. Partial scapular retraction will help stabilize the shoulder girdle. These exercises may not be appropriate for those with orthopedic concerns associated with the wrist.

VARIATIONS AND COMMENTS: For more strength, balance and stabilization challenge, lift one foot off the floor and extend the leg in front of the body (See Fig. 101). Hold one leg up while performing multiple repetitions (alternate sides midway through the reps), or alternately lift a leg with each repetition of scapular depression.

Fig. 101

EXERCISE GOAL: The goal of these exercises is to challenge muscular endurance and strength in the triceps, anterior deltoids, pectoralis major and lower trapezius, as well as dynamic balance, core stabilization, shoulder and shoulder girdle stabilization.

SETUP AND ALIGNMENT: Sit with the hips centered on the top of the dome. Flex the knees and rest the feet flat on the floor, about hip width apart. Place the hands on the sides of the dome with the fingers facing down. Fully extend the elbows, lifting the hips off the dome. Walk the feet forward until the hips are aligned over the front third of the dome (See Fig. 102). Align the shoulders over the wrists in this starting position.

Fig. 102

PERFORMING THE EXERCISE: Slowly flex the elbows and extend the shoulders, lowering the body until approximately 90 degrees of elbow flexion (or less) is reached (See Fig. 103). Pause at the bottom of the movement. Then, extend the elbows and flex the shoulders, pressing back up to the starting position. Repeat for the appropriate number of repetitions.

Fig. 103

SAFETY CONSIDERATIONS: Avoid flexing the elbows to an angle that is deeper than 90 degrees. An extreme angle can cause stress to the shoulder joint. Do not use the legs or hips to push the body up. Instead, stabilize the trunk and isolate the movement in the upper arm and shoulder regions. Maintain neutral lumbar and cervical posture throughout the exercise. Partial scapular retraction and scapular depression will help stabilize the shoulder girdle. These exercises may not be appropriate for those with orthopedic concerns associated with the wrist or shoulder.

VARIATIONS AND COMMENTS: For more strength, balance and stabilization challenge, extend both knees in the starting position and rest the heels on the floor. Slowly flex the elbows and extend the shoulders, lowering the body until approximately 90 degrees of elbow flexion (or less) is reached (See Fig. 104). Pause at the bottom of the movement. Then, extend the elbows and flex the shoulders, pressing back up to the starting position (See Fig. 105). Repeat for the appropriate number of repetitions.

Fig. 104

Fig. 105

EXERCISE GOAL: The goal of these exercises is to challenge muscular endurance and strength in the triceps, anterior deltoids, pectoralis major, lower trapezius and hip extensor group, as well as dynamic balance, core stabilization, shoulder and shoulder girdle stabilization.

SETUP AND ALIGNMENT: Sit with the hips centered on the top of the dome. Extend the knees and rest the heels on the floor. Place the hands on the sides of the dome with the fingers facing down. Fully extend the elbows, lifting the hips off the dome. Walk the feet forward until the hips are aligned over the front third of the dome. Align the shoulders over the wrists in this starting position.

PERFORMING THE EXERCISE: Slowly flex the elbows and extend the shoulders, lowering the body until approximately 90 degrees of elbow flexion (or less) is reached (See Fig. 106). Pause at the bottom of the movement. Then, extend the elbows and flex the shoulders, while simultaneously extending the hips (See Fig. 107). Repeat for the appropriate number of repetitions.

SAFETY CONSIDERATIONS: Do not hyperextend the lumbar spine while extending the hips. When full hip extension is reached at the top of the movement, neutral lumbar and cervical posture should be maintained. Avoid flexing the elbows to an angle that is deeper than 90 degrees. An extreme angle can cause stress to the shoulder joint. Do not use the legs or the hips to push the body up. Instead, stabilize the trunk and isolate the movement in the upper arm and shoulder region. Partial scapular retraction and scapular depression will help stabilize the shoulder girdle. These exercises may not be appropriate for those with orthopedic concerns associated with the wrist or shoulder.

VARIATIONS AND COMMENTS: For more strength, balance and stabilization challenge, lift one leg off the floor while performing the elbow and hip extension (See Fig. 108). Hold one leg up while performing multiple repetitions (alternate sides midway through the reps), or alternately lift a leg with each elbow/hip extension repetition. Repeat for the appropriate number of repetitions.

Fig. 108

Fig. 106

Fig. 107

EXERCISE GOAL: The goal of this exercise is to challenge muscular endurance and strength in the trapezius (parts II, III and IV) and rhomboids, as well as dynamic balance, core stabilization, hip, shoulder and shoulder girdle stabilization.

SETUP AND ALIGNMENT: Sit with the hips centered on the top of the dome. Flex the knees and rest the feet flat on the floor, about hip width apart. Place the hands on the sides of the dome with the fingers facing down. Fully extend the elbows. Partially extend the hips, lifting them off the dome. Walk the feet forward until the hips are aligned over the front third of the dome. Align the shoulders over the wrists in this starting position (See Fig. 109).

PERFORMING THE EXERCISE: Move one hand and one foot at a time, walking in a circle around the dome and base (See Fig. 110). Reverse the direction after a circle has been completed.

Fig. 110

Fig. 109

SAFETY CONSIDERATIONS: Adjust hand placement on the dome to find the most comfortable position for the wrists. Maintain neutral lumbar and cervical posture throughout the exercise. Partial scapular retraction and scapular depression will help stabilize the shoulder girdle. These exercises may not be appropriate for those with orthopedic concerns associated with the wrist.

VARIATIONS AND COMMENTS: For more vestibular challenge, close the eyes while performing the "walk-arounds."

EXERCISE GOAL: The goal of these exercises is to challenge muscular endurance of the abductor and adductor groups, as well as kneeling dynamic balance, core stabilization, and hip stabilization.

SETUP AND ALIGNMENT: Kneel with one knee centered on the top of the dome. Place the other leg out to the side of the body with the toes touching the floor. For balance assistance, the toes of the flexed leg may touch the floor. For more balance challenge, lift the toes off the floor. Place the arms out to the sides at about waist height for balance assistance, or the hands on the hips for more balance challenge. Align the body in "centered" position from the knee through the top of the head (See Fig. 111).

Fig. 111

PERFORMING THE EXERCISE: Abduct the extended leg to a height where "centered" position can still be maintained. Adjust arm positioning to maintain body position and balance (See Fig. 112). Pause at the top of the movement. Then, slowly lower the leg back to the starting position. Repeat for the appropriate number of repetitions.

Fig. 112

SAFETY CONSIDERATIONS: Maintain neutral spinal alignment in both the lumbar and cervical spine. Avoid excessively tipping the shoulders and pelvis to either side while the weight is on one leg. Contracting the core musculature will enhance balance performance. Centering the front of the lower leg across the top of the dome will help avoid unnecessary pressure on the kneecap, and makes balancing easier.

VARIATIONS AND COMMENTS: For more balance and stabilization challenge, begin in the same starting position, but reach out diagonally in front of the body with both arms (See Fig. 113). Flex the knee and pull it in toward the waist, while simultaneously rotating the torso and pulling the arms into the waist (See Fig. 114). Repeat for the appropriate number of repetitions, on both sides.

Fig. 113

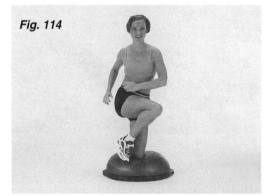

Fig. 114

EXERCISE GOAL: The goal of these exercises is to challenge muscular endurance and strength in the hip extensor group, as well as prone dynamic balance, core stabilization, and shoulder girdle stabilization.

SETUP AND ALIGNMENT: Lie prone with the hips and abdomen centered on the dome. Rest the lower arms on the floor. Fully extend the knees, resting the toes on the floor.

PERFORMING THE EXERCISE: Slowly extend one hip, lifting the leg off the floor (See Fig. 115). Pause at the top of the movement. Then, slowly lower back to the starting position. Repeat on one side or alternate sides for the appropriate number of repetitions. When this variation feels balanced and stable, progress to double leg hip extension. Simultaneously extend both hips and lift the legs to the point of full hip extension (See Fig. 116). Repeat for the appropriate number of repetitions.

SAFETY CONSIDERATIONS: Maintain neutral lumbar and cervical posture. Do not extend the lumbar spine while extending the hips. Partial scapular retraction will help stabilize the shoulder girdle and isolate the work in the hip region. Avoid using momentum or ballistic movement to extend the spine. Keep the movement smooth and controlled.

VARIATIONS AND COMMENTS: For more balance and stabilization challenge, perform the double leg hip extension while simultaneously reaching forward with both arms (See Fig. 117). Hold the arms and trunk in a stable position while lifting the legs. The focus of this variation is on challenging balance while extending the hips. Do not perform lumbar spinal extension with the hip extension.

Fig. 117

Fig. 115

Fig. 116

EXERCISE GOAL: The goal of these exercises is to challenge muscular endurance and strength in the hip abductor group, as well as sidelying dynamic balance, core stabilization, hip and shoulder girdle stabilization.

SETUP AND ALIGNMENT: Lie on one side on the floor with the lower arm resting on top of the dome. Align the elbow directly under the shoulder. Flex the knees approximately 90 degrees and place them in line with the hips. Align the knees, hips and shoulders with one another.

PERFORMING THE EXERCISE: Slowly lift the hips off the floor until the trunk is in a straight line from the knees through the shoulders (See Fig. 118). When this variation feels stable and balanced, progress to a hip lift with the legs placed in an extended "scissor" position (See Fig. 119), or in an extended aligned position (See Fig. 120). Pause at the top of the movement. Then, slowly lower back to the starting position. Repeat for the appropriate number of repetitions.

SAFETY CONSIDERATIONS: Keep the shoulders and hips aligned over one another. Do not let the top hip or shoulder roll forward or back. Attempt to maintain neutral lumbar and cervical alignment. Isometric adduction of the legs will help stabilize the pelvis, while partial scapular retraction will help stabilize the shoulder girdle.

VARIATIONS AND COMMENTS: For more strength, balance and stabilization challenge, simultaneously abduct the top leg while lifting the hips (See Fig. 121). Pause and balance at the top of the movement. Then lower both the leg and the hips back to the starting position.

Fig. 118

Fig. 119

Fig. 120

Fig. 121

CARDIOVASCULAR & ATHLETIC DRILLS

Following is a small sampling of the hundreds of cardiovascular movement patterns and athletic drills that can be performed on the BOSU. Athletic drills, step movement patterns, cardio kickboxing or fitness martial arts movements can all be integrated with balance and stabilization challenges.

SQUAT DRILLS

EXERCISE GOAL: The goal of these exercises is to challenge the cardiorespiratory system, as well as standing dynamic balance, agility, core stabilization, foot and ankle stabilization, and balance related to the vestibular system.

SETUP AND ALIGNMENT: Stand in "centered" position on top of the dome with the feet about hip width apart or slightly narrower. Place the arms out to the sides at about waist height for balance assistance, or place the hands on the hips for more balance challenge (See Fig. 122).

PERFORMING THE EXERCISE: Flex at the hips and knees and perform a squat movement. Reach forward with the arms to counterbalance the backward movement of the hips. Pause at the bottom of the movement. Then, slowly extend the knees and hips and return to "centered" position. When the basic squat movement feels balanced and stable, progress to a squat with alternating compressions. Hold the squat at the bottom of the movement and press one foot down into the dome while simultaneously un-weighting the other foot (See Fig. 123). Repeat for the appropriate number of repetitions.

SAFETY CONSIDERATIONS: The depth of the squat should be determined by proper alignment, balance and the ability to control the movement. Attempt to maintain level foot positioning when standing on the dome. Avoid excessive dorsi flexion, plantar flexion, inversion or eversion. Move smoothly while performing the alternating compressions, without introducing excessive reaction from the trunk or upper body. Begin the weight shifting movements with small range of motion, then increase range of motion as skill level, balance and control improve.

VARIATIONS AND COMMENTS: For more balance, stabilization and proprioceptive challenge, the squat can be performed with simultaneous trunk rotation. While rotating the trunk, the hands can reach for the outside of the knee (See Fig. 124), calf, ankle or side of the dome. Alternate sides with each squat/trunk rotation. Visually tracking the hand touch on the knee, calf, ankle or dome will add vestibular challenge. For additional balance and stabilization challenge, squat from the "centered" position, then simultaneously extend one leg and abduct the other (See Fig. 125). Alternate sides for the appropriate number of repetitions.

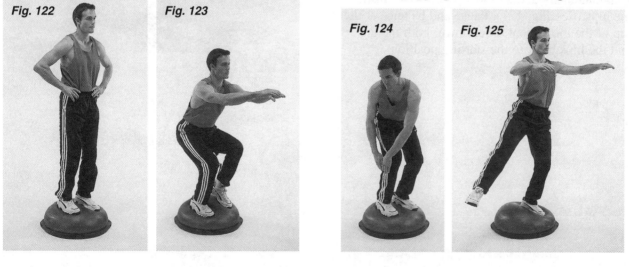

Fig. 122   Fig. 123   Fig. 124   Fig. 125

EXERCISE GOAL: The goal of these exercises is to challenge the cardiorespiratory system, as well as standing dynamic balance, agility, core stabilization, foot and ankle stabilization, and balance related to the vestibular system.

SETUP AND ALIGNMENT: Stand on top of the dome in "centered" position. Then, place one foot in the middle of the dome and shift all the weight onto this foot. Place the other foot against the side of the dome for balance. The arms may be extended out to the sides at about waist height for balance assistance, or the hands may rest on the hips for more balance challenge.

PERFORMING THE EXERCISE: Flex the knee of the weight bearing leg slightly. Move the other leg in a circular pattern, tapping the front, side (See Fig. 126) and back of the dome lightly with the foot. When balance and stabilization can be maintained with this tapping variation, progress to single low kicks to the front, side and back (See Fig. 127). Alternate sides, performing an equal number of repetitions on each side.

SAFETY CONSIDERATIONS: Attempt to maintain level foot positioning when standing on the dome. Avoid excessive dorsi flexion, plantar flexion, inversion or eversion. Move smoothly while performing the low kicks, without excessive reaction from the trunk or upper body. Begin the kicking movements with small range of motion. Then, increase range of motion as skill level, balance and control improve. Maintain neutral lumbar and cervical posture throughout the exercises.

VARIATIONS AND COMMENTS: For more balance and stabilization challenge, bend the weight bearing leg slightly and perform multiple kicks (3 to 5 low kicks in each position) to the front, side and back. To add vestibular challenge, visually track the leg when performing single taps or kicks in any direction, or close the eyes during any of the variations.

Fig. 126   Fig. 127

EXERCISE GOAL: The goal of these exercises is to challenge the cardiorespiratory system, as well as standing dynamic balance, agility, core stabilization, foot and ankle stabilization, and balance related to the vestibular system.

SETUP AND ALIGNMENT: Stand on top of the dome with the feet about hip width apart or slightly narrower. Place the arms out to the sides at about waist height for balance assistance, or place the hands on the hips for more balance challenge.

PERFORMING THE EXERCISE: From this "centered" position, step down to the floor with one leg into a side squat lunge movement. Reach forward with the arms to counterbalance the backward movement of the hips (See Fig. 128). Pause at the bottom of the movement. Then, press back up to "centered" position on top of the dome. Repeat for multiple repetitions on one side, or alternate sides for the appropriate number of repetitions. When the "Side Squat Lunge" feels balanced and stable, progress to the "Side Tap Lunge" or the "Back Tap Lunge." Keeping the weight centered over the dome, flex the knee of the weight bearing leg, and tap the foot of the non-weight bearing leg to the side (See Fig. 129) or to the back (See Fig. 130). The arms may reach forward or side, counterbalancing the "lunging" leg. Alternate sides for the appropriate number of repetitions.

SAFETY CONSIDERATIONS: When performing "Side Squat Lunges," the weight shifts to the outside leg during the lunge, then back to equal weight between both feet when standing on top of the dome. When performing "Side Tap Lunges," or "Back Tap Lunges," the weight is on the supporting leg during the lunge, and then equally distributed when standing on top of the dome. Attempt to maintain level foot positioning when standing on the dome. Avoid excessive dorsi flexion, plantar flexion, inversion or eversion. Begin the lunging movements with small range of motion. Then, increase range of motion as skill level, balance and control improve. Maintain neutral lumbar and cervical posture throughout the exercises.

VARIATIONS AND COMMENTS: For more balance, stabilization and agility challenge, alternate sides with a propulsive leap onto the dome while changing sides. Variations in cadence and range of motion will add balance and agility challenges. For added vestibular challenge, visually track the leg that is lunging to the side.

Fig. 128   *Fig. 129*   *Fig. 130*

EXERCISE GOAL: The goal of these exercises is to challenge the cardiorespiratory system, as well as standing dynamic balance, agility, core stabilization, foot and ankle stabilization, and balance related to the vestibular system.

SETUP AND ALIGNMENT: Stand on top of the dome with the feet about hip width apart or slightly narrower. Place the arms out to the sides at about waist height for balance assistance, or place the hands on the hips for more balance challenge.

PERFORMING THE EXERCISE: From this "centered" position, flex the knee of the weight bearing leg, and tap the foot of the non-weight bearing leg to the side or diagonally to the back. Reach diagonally up with the arms to counter-balance the "lunging" leg (See Fig. 131). Then, pull the non-weight bearing leg up into a knee lift, while simultaneously pulling the arms in toward the waist (See Fig. 132). Repeat for the appropriate number of repetitions.

SAFETY CONSIDERATIONS: Balance and center the body on top of the dome during each knee lift. Attempt to maintain level foot positioning with the foot that is placed on the dome. Avoid excessive dorsi flexion, plantar flexion, inversion or eversion. Begin the lunging knee lifts with small range of motion. Then, increase range of motion as skill level, balance and control improve.

VARIATIONS AND COMMENTS: For more balance, stabilization and proprioceptive challenge, perform the lunging knee lift while simultaneously rotating the trunk toward the lifting knee (See Fig. 133). Allow the head to turn to the side as the torso rotates for more vestibular challenge. Perform multiple repetitions on one side, then change sides for the appropriate number of repetitions.

Fig. 133

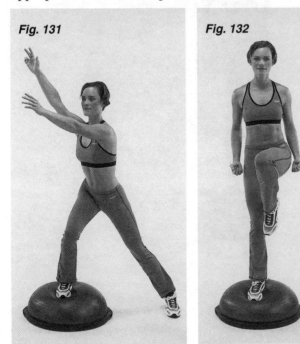

Fig. 131

Fig. 132

EXERCISE GOAL: The goal of these exercises is to challenge the cardiorespiratory system, as well as standing dynamic balance, agility, core stabilization, and foot and ankle stabilization.

SETUP AND ALIGNMENT: Stand on top of the dome with the feet about hip width apart or slightly narrower. Place the arms out to the sides at about waist height for balance assistance, or place the hands on the hips for more balance challenge.

PERFORMING THE EXERCISE: Step down to the floor, one foot at a time, into a straddle position. Reach forward or side with the arms to counterbalance the leg position (See Fig. 134). Step up onto the dome with one foot, then lift the opposite knee. Pull the arms in toward the waist as the knee lifts (See Fig. 135). Step back down into the straddle, one foot at a time, leading with the leg that is lifted. Repeat this 4-count movement, alternating sides, for the appropriate number of repetitions.

SAFETY CONSIDERATIONS: Stepping down slightly behind the center of the platform, instead of in line with the center, can modify the width of the straddle. A narrower width can be achieved by stepping further to the back. Balance and center the body on top of the dome during each knee lift. Attempt to maintain level foot positioning with the foot that is placed on the dome. Avoid excessive dorsi flexion, plantar flexion, inversion or eversion. Maintain neutral lumbar and cervical posture throughout the exercises.

VARIATIONS AND COMMENTS: For more cardiorespiratory, balance and stabilization challenge, add a propulsive hop during the knee lift phase of the movement (See Fig. 136). The knee lift can be varied by using front kicks, side lifts (abduction), hip extension or leg curls to the back. Alternate sides and repeat for the appropriate number of repetitions.

Fig. 136

Fig. 134

Fig. 135

EXERCISE GOAL: The goal of these exercises is to challenge the cardiorespiratory system, as well as standing dynamic balance, agility, core stabilization, foot and ankle stabilization, and balance related to the vestibular system.

SETUP AND ALIGNMENT: Stand on the floor to one side of the base, facing front.

PERFORMING THE EXERCISE: Place one foot on the dome in preparation to step up. Reach forward with the arms to counterbalance the leg movement (See Fig. 137). Step up onto the dome and simultaneously lift the opposite knee while pulling the arms in toward the waist (See Fig. 138). Step back down to the floor with the leg that was lifted. Then, lean back slightly and lift the opposite leg into a front kick position (See Fig. 139). Repeat for the appropriate number of repetitions, then change sides and repeat for an equal number of repetitions.

SAFETY CONSIDERATIONS: Balance and center the body on top of the dome during each knee lift. Attempt to maintain level foot positioning with the foot that is placed on the dome. Avoid excessive dorsi flexion, plantar flexion, inversion or eversion. Begin the movements with small range of motion. Then, increase range of motion as skill level, balance and control improve.

VARIATIONS AND COMMENTS: For an easier modification, a knee lift may be substituted for the front kick. For more cardiorespiratory, balance and stabilization challenge, add a propulsive hop during the knee lift phase of the movement. Repeat for the appropriate number of repetitions on both sides.

Fig. 137

Fig. 138

Fig. 139

EXERCISE GOAL: The goal of these exercises is to challenge the cardiorespiratory system, as well as standing dynamic balance, agility, core stabilization, foot and ankle stabilization, and balance related to the vestibular system.

SETUP AND ALIGNMENT: Stand on the floor to one side of the base, facing front.

PERFORMING THE EXERCISE: Place one foot on top of the dome and flex both knees in preparation to jump. Reach forward or side with the arms in a "ready" position (See Fig. 140). Jump up and slightly to the side, so that the body is centered over the dome (See Fig. 141). Land with both feet on top of the dome and "stick" the landing with no extraneous movement (See Fig. 142). Continue repetitions on the same side, or step off to the opposite side and repeat the "jump-stick" for the appropriate number of repetitions.

SAFETY CONSIDERATIONS: Begin the jumping movements with small range of motion. Then, increase range of motion as skill level, balance and control improve. Balance and center the body on top of the dome after each jump. Attempt to maintain level foot positioning with both feet on the dome. Avoid excessive dorsi flexion, plantar flexion, inversion or eversion. Maintain neutral lumbar and cervical posture throughout the exercises.

VARIATIONS AND COMMENTS: The "jump-stick" movement can be performed as a transitional move between any exercises or drills performed on top of the dome. For example, perform a squat with rotation to one side, "jump-stick" two times on top of the dome, then squat with rotation to the other side. Jogging or running with high-knees on top of the dome can be interspersed with "jump-stick" drills. For more balance and proprioceptive challenge, jump and turn 45, 90, 180 or 360 degrees. Begin with small range jump-turns. Then, when "centered" position can be maintained during the jump and landing, progress to greater range of motion jump-turns.

Fig. 140

Fig. 141

Fig. 142

STATIC STRETCHES

• • • • •

ANTERIOR TRUNK STRETCH

EXERCISE GOAL: The goal of this exercise is to challenge flexibility in the rectus abdominis, internal/external obliques, pectoralis major and anterior deltoids, as well as supine balance and core stabilization.

SETUP AND ALIGNMENT: Lie supine with the thoracic spine centered on the dome and the hips resting lightly on the floor in front of the platform. Flex the knees and place the feet flat on the floor, about hip width apart. Place the hands behind the head and support the neck in neutral position.

PERFORMING THE EXERCISE: Slowly extend the cervical spine until the back of the head is resting on the dome. Release the hands from behind the head and open the arms to the sides, in line with the shoulders (See Fig. 143). Relax into this passive stretch and hold for 10 to 60 seconds.

SAFETY CONSIDERATIONS: For those with orthopedic concerns of the cervical spine, keep the hands behind the head and maintain neutral position. Adjust the spine up or down on the dome until a comfortable position is attained.

VARIATIONS AND COMMENTS: For more flexibility and balance challenge, lie supine with the lumbar spine centered on the dome. Flex the knees approximately 90 degrees and place the feet flat on the floor, about hip width apart. For more balance challenge, move the feet close together. Place the hands behind the head and support the neck in a neutral or slightly extended position (See Fig. 144). Relax into this passive stretch and hold for 10 to 60 seconds. For additional stretch in the hip flexor muscle group, extend the knees and hips while holding the previous stretch.

Fig. 144

Fig. 143

EXERCISE GOAL: The goal of this exercise is to challenge flexibility in the lumbar spinal extensor group, trapezius, rhomboids, posterior deltoids and latissimus dorsi (only in variation 2), as well as prone balance and core stabilization.

SETUP AND ALIGNMENT: Lie prone with the hips and abdomen centered on the dome. Place the hands on the floor in front of the platform. Flex the knees, and rest the lower legs and toes on the floor.

PERFORMING THE EXERCISE: Slowly flex the cervical spine until the forehead rests lightly on the floor in front of the dome. Wrap the arms around the sides of the platform, releasing through the thoracic and lumbar spine (See Fig. 145). Relax into this passive stretch and hold for 10 to 60 seconds.

Fig. 145

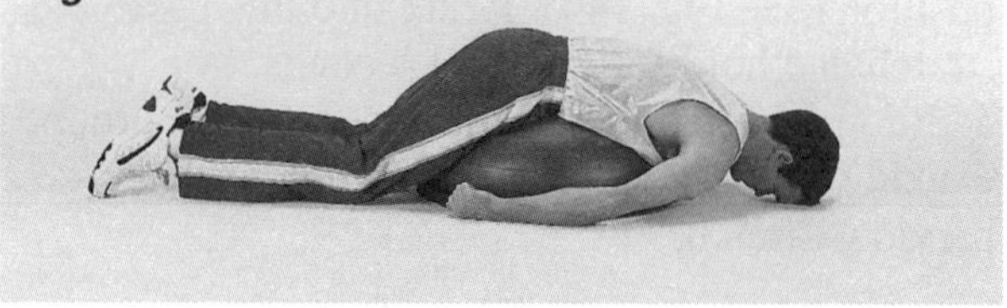

SAFETY CONSIDERATIONS: For more neck support, place the hands under the forehead with the elbows open to the sides. Keep the knees about hip width apart for balance assistance, or move the knees close together for more balance challenge.

VARIATIONS AND COMMENTS: For more flexibility challenge, flex the shoulders and reach overhead with the arms. Rest the hands on the floor (See Fig. 146). This variation will increase the stretch on the latissimus dorsi.

Fig. 146

EXERCISE GOAL: The goal of this exercise is to challenge flexibility in the lumbar spinal extensor group, latissimus dorsi, trapezius, rhomboids and posterior deltoids, as well as dynamic balance and core stabilization.

SETUP AND ALIGNMENT: Kneel on the floor, on a mat or other padded surface. Turn the BOSU to a "platform side up" position. Grasp the handles on the sides of the platform. Adjust body positioning so that the knees and feet are approximately hip width apart and the shoulders and chest are aligned over the center of the platform. Align the hips directly over the knees.

PERFORMING THE EXERCISE: Keeping the hips lifted, slowly pull the hips back toward the heels. Perform a slight posterior pelvic tilt to enhance the stretch in the lumbar spine. Flex at the shoulder joints and pull the upper body back away from the platform (See Fig. 147). When the shoulders are fully flexed, let the upper body sink passively into the stretch, while continuing to actively lengthen the spine. Relax into this active/passive stretch and hold for 10 to 60 seconds.

SAFETY CONSIDERATIONS: Avoid passively "sitting on the heels" with the hips. Excessive, loaded knee flexion may cause stress to the knee joint. Keep the hips lifted off the heels and focus on lengthening the spine while pulling back. Maintain neutral posture in the cervical spine throughout the stretch.

VARIATIONS AND COMMENTS: For more flexibility, balance and stabilization challenge, flex the shoulders and pull the hips back toward the heels, while simultaneously tilting the platform to one side (See Fig. 148). Hold the stretch in the tilted position for 10 to 60 seconds. Then return to the starting position and repeat the tilting stretch on the other side. For a more dynamic stretch, slowly tilt or rock the platform side to side while holding the flexed shoulder position.

Fig. 148

Fig. 147

EXERCISE GOAL: The goal of this exercise is to challenge flexibility in the rectus abdominis, internal/external obliques, pectoralis major, anterior deltoids and gluteus medius, as well as core stabilization.

SETUP AND ALIGNMENT: Lie supine on the floor with the hips close to the platform. Flex both knees approximately 90 degrees. Place one foot on top of the dome and the other foot on the floor next to the platform. Open the arms to the sides, placing the palms on the floor at a level that is just lower than shoulder height.

PERFORMING THE EXERCISE: Rotating the trunk, slowly lower the legs to one side. Lower them in the direction of the foot that is placed on the floor (See Fig. 149). Let the bottom leg rest on the floor. Gently pull the top leg down (adduct and internally rotate) toward the bottom leg until an appropriate stretch is felt. Relax into this active/passive stretch and hold for 10 to 60 seconds. Roll back to the starting position and repeat the stretch on the opposite side.

Fig. 149

SAFETY CONSIDERATIONS: If there is excessive hyperextension in the lumbar spine, adjust the leg position by flexing the hips to a greater degree, or by rotating the trunk through a smaller range of motion. Move the knees up toward the trunk or down toward the feet to modify or increase the flexibility challenge. Maintain neutral posture in the cervical spine throughout the stretch.

VARIATIONS AND COMMENTS: For more flexibility and core stabilization challenge, hold the leg position of the rotary trunk stretch and slowly lift the arms overhead. Actively stretch the arms in the opposite direction that the legs are rotating (See Fig. 150). Relax into this active/passive stretch and hold for 10 to 60 seconds. Roll back to the starting position and repeat the stretch on the opposite side.

Fig. 150

EXERCISE GOAL: The goal of this exercise is to challenge flexibility in the rectus abdominis, internal/external obliques, pectoralis major, anterior deltoids and iliotibial band and hamstrings, as well as core stabilization.

SETUP AND ALIGNMENT: Lie supine on the floor with the hips close to the platform. Flex the knees approximately 90 degrees. Place both feet on top of the dome, about hip width apart. Open the arms to the sides, placing the palms on the floor at a level that is just lower than shoulder height.

PERFORMING THE EXERCISE: Rotating the trunk, slowly lower the legs to one side. When the thigh and knee of the bottom leg touch the floor, further flex the hip of the top leg and lower that leg toward the floor (See Fig. 151). Gently pull the top leg down (adduct) toward the bottom leg until an appropriate stretch is felt. Relax into this active/passive stretch and hold for 10 to 60 seconds. Roll back to the starting position and repeat the stretch on the opposite side.

SAFETY CONSIDERATIONS: Attempt to maintain approximately 90 degrees of flexion in the upper leg. If there is excessive hyperextension in the lumbar spine, adjust the leg position by flexing the hip of the lower leg to a greater degree, or by rotating the trunk through a smaller range of motion. Maintain neutral posture in the cervical spine throughout the stretch.

VARIATIONS AND COMMENTS: For more flexibility challenge, extend the knee of the top leg and rest the toes on the floor. Maintain approximately 90 degrees of hip flexion to maximize the iliotibial band stretch. The stretch can be performed actively by holding the top leg in its extended position, or can be performed passively by holding the back of the calf or thigh with the hand (See Fig. 152). Hold the stretch for 10 to 60 seconds. Then, roll back to the starting position and repeat the stretch on the opposite side.

Fig. 152

Fig. 151

EXERCISE GOAL: The goal of this exercise is to challenge flexibility in the pectoralis major, anterior deltoids and biceps, as well as core stabilization.

SETUP AND ALIGNMENT: Sit upright on the floor in front of the platform. Flex the knees approximately 90 degrees and rest the feet on the floor. Place the hands on the knees.

PERFORMING THE EXERCISE: Reach behind the body with one arm and place the hand on top of the dome, slightly behind center. Rotate the torso slightly (about 45 degrees or less) to the side, in the direction of the arm. Place the other arm across the knees for stabilization (See Fig. 153). Relax and hold this stretch for 10 to 60 seconds. Return to the starting position and repeat the stretch on the other side.

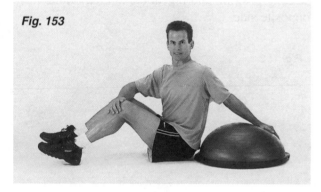

Fig. 153

SAFETY CONSIDERATIONS: Adjust hand placement on the dome to maximize the stretch in the chest, shoulder and upper arm. Slide the hand back for more stretch, or forward for less. Maintain neutral lumbar and cervical spinal posture throughout the stretch. Do not flex or round the lower back while rotating the spine. Sitting on the floor may not be appropriate for those who have orthopedic concerns associated with the lower back. A variation of this stretch may be performed by sitting on top of the dome and actively reaching behind the body with one or both arms.

VARIATIONS AND COMMENTS: For more flexibility and core stabilization challenge, rotate the trunk to the front while keeping one arm behind and the hand on the dome. Place the opposite hand on the same side thigh (See Fig. 154). Relax and hold this stretch for 10 to 60 seconds. Return to the starting position and repeat the stretch on the other side.

Fig. 154

SEATED HAMSTRINGS, GASTROCNEMIUS STRETCH

EXERCISE GOAL: The goal of this exercise is to challenge flexibility in the hamstrings group, gastrocnemius and soleus, as well as seated balance and core stabilization.

SETUP AND ALIGNMENT: Sit upright with the hips centered on top of the dome. Extend one leg out in front of the body with the heel resting on the floor. Flex the knee of the opposite leg and place the foot on the floor. Rest the hands on the thighs or knees.

PERFORMING THE EXERCISE: Lean forward slightly from the hips until a stretch is felt in the hamstrings. Begin to dorsi flex the ankle (pull the toe toward the shin) of the extended leg until a stretch is felt in the calf region (See Fig. 155). Relax and hold this active stretch for 10 to 60 seconds. Return to an upright, seated position, extend the opposite leg and repeat the stretch on the other side.

SAFETY CONSIDERATIONS: Do not flex the lumbar spine while flexing forward from the hips. Maintain neutral lumbar and cervical posture throughout the stretch. A slight anterior pelvic tilt will help attain and maintain neutral lumbar posture in the seated position.

VARIATIONS AND COMMENTS: For more flexibility challenge, flex further forward at the hips and dorsi flex the ankle to a further range of motion. Reach forward with the same arm as the extended leg and grasp the toes (See Fig. 156). Hold this deeper, active/passive stretch for 10 to 60 seconds. Return to an upright, seated position, extend the opposite leg and repeat the stretch on the other side.

Fig. 156

Fig. 155

EXERCISE GOAL: The goal of this exercise is to challenge flexibility in the adductors and hamstrings groups, as well as seated balance and core stabilization.

SETUP AND ALIGNMENT: Sit upright with the hips centered on top of the dome. Extend one leg forward and out to the side at an approximate 45 degree angle from the midline of the body. Flex the knee of the opposite leg and place the foot on the floor near the platform. Place the hands on the sides of the dome, next to or slightly behind the hips.

PERFORMING THE EXERCISE: Slowly flex forward from the hips until a stretch is felt in both the adductor and hamstrings groups of the extended leg. Pressing down gently into the dome with the arms will help stabilize the trunk and keep the spine extended (See Fig. 157). Relax and hold this stretch for 10 to 60 seconds. Return to an upright, seated position, extend the opposite leg and repeat the stretch on the other side.

Fig. 157

SAFETY CONSIDERATIONS: Do not flex the lumbar spine while flexing forward from the hips. Maintain neutral lumbar and cervical posture throughout the stretch. A slight anterior tilt will help attain and maintain neutral lumbar posture in the seated position. Dorsi flexing the ankle of the extended leg(s) is acceptable if additional stretch in the gastrocnemius is desired. If tightness in the calf region is a limiting factor for creating an effective stretch for the adductors and hamstrings, plantar flex the ankle(s).

VARIATIONS AND COMMENTS: For more flexibility and stabilization challenge, extend both legs out to the side in a straddle position, at an approximate 45 degree angle from the midline of the body. Slowly flex forward from the hips until a stretch is felt in both the adductor and hamstrings groups. Press the arms gently into the dome to help extend and stabilize the spine (See Fig. 158). For more stabilization challenge, release the arms and reach forward in front of the chest while flexing forward from the hips. (Note: Generally, a wider straddle position will result in more adductor stretch and less hamstrings stretch. A narrower position will result in more hamstrings stretch and less adductor stretch.)

Fig. 158

EXERCISE GOAL: The goal of this exercise is to challenge flexibility in the gluteal group and internal rotator group, as well as seated balance and core stabilization.

SETUP AND ALIGNMENT: Sit upright with the hips centered on top of the dome. Extend one leg out in front of the body with the heel resting on the floor. Flex the knee of the opposite leg and place the foot on the floor. Rest the hands on the thighs or knees.

PERFORMING THE EXERCISE: Lift the leg with the flexed knee. Externally rotate at the hip and place the outside of the ankle on the opposite thigh, just above the knee. Place the hands on the knee and foot of the flexed, externally rotated leg to help stabilize the spine and to help hold the leg in position. Flex forward slightly from the hips (See Fig. 159). Actively, externally rotate the flexed leg. Hold this active stretch for 10 to 60 seconds. Release the leg, extend the other leg, and repeat the stretch on the other side.

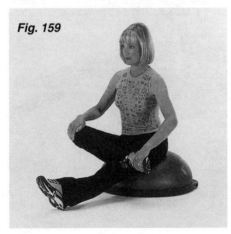
Fig. 159

SAFETY CONSIDERATIONS: Do not flex the lumbar spine while sitting upright or flexing forward from the hips. Maintain neutral lumbar and cervical posture throughout the stretch. A slight anterior tilt will help attain and maintain neutral lumbar posture in the seated position. Avoid placing the ankle of the flexed leg directly on top of the extended knee. Instead, place the ankle on the thigh, above the knee.

VARIATIONS AND COMMENTS: For more flexibility challenge, slowly flex the knee of the extended leg while maintaining external rotation of the lifted leg. Flex further forward from the hips (See Fig. 160). Continue to externally rotate the leg actively, or use the hands to press the knee further open for a more passive stretch. Hold the stretch for 10 to 60 seconds. Release the leg, extend the other leg, and repeat the stretch on the other side.

Fig. 160

EXERCISE GOAL: The goal of this exercise is to challenge flexibility in the external rotator group and gluteal group, as well as seated balance and core stabilization.

SETUP AND ALIGNMENT: Sit upright with the hips centered on top of the dome. Flex the knees approximately 90 degrees and place the feet on the floor, a little wider than shoulder width apart. Place the hands on the sides of the dome, next to or slightly behind the hips.

PERFORMING THE EXERCISE: Internally rotate both hips, until the knees and inner thighs are close together and a stretch is felt in the external rotators and hip region. Allow the feet to roll to the inside edge of the shoe or foot (See Fig. 161). Relax and hold this passive stretch for 10 to 60 seconds.

SAFETY CONSIDERATIONS: Maintain neutral ankle alignment while internally rotating the hips. Do not "collapse" the inner ankles toward the floor. Do not flex the lumbar spine while sitting upright. Maintain neutral lumbar and cervical posture throughout the stretch. A slight anterior tilt will help attain and maintain neutral lumbar posture in the seated position. Extending the elbows and pressing the hands down gently into the dome, will help stabilize and extend the spine.

VARIATIONS AND COMMENTS: For more flexibility challenge, "bias" the stretch by internally rotating one leg until the hip begins to lift slightly off the dome. Then, internally rotate the other leg, "folding" the leg over the thigh of the first (See Fig. 162). Hold this stretch for 10 to 60 seconds. Repeat the stretch on the other side.

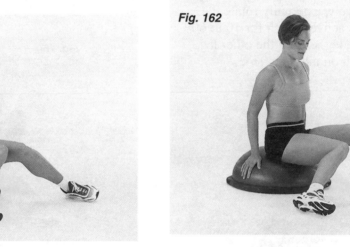

Fig. 161

Fig. 162

EXERCISE GOAL: The goal of this exercise is to challenge flexibility in the hip flexor and quadriceps groups, as well as supine balance and core stabilization.

SETUP AND ALIGNMENT: Sit on the floor and rest the upper back against the side of the dome. Center the thoracic spine, shoulders and neck on the top of the dome and slowly lift the hips until the upper thighs are almost parallel to the floor. Adjust the feet until they are approximately hip width apart, with the heels aligned under the knees. Place the hands on the floor under the hips.

PERFORMING THE EXERCISE: Contract the gluteals and fully extend the hips, until a stretch is felt in the hip flexors and quadriceps. Lift the hands off the floor and place them on the hips (See Fig. 163). Hold this active stretch for 10 to 60 seconds, then release by slowly lowering the hips back to the floor.

Fig. 163

SAFETY CONSIDERATIONS: Fully extend the hips, but do not extend the lumbar spine in the bridge position. Maintain neutral lumbar and cervical posture. Adjust body positioning on the dome so that the neck is relaxed in a neutral position. If the upper torso is too far forward on the dome, the cervical spine will excessively flex.

VARIATIONS AND COMMENTS: For more flexibility challenge in the quadriceps group, lower the hips slightly and slide one heel in closer to the dome, while still keeping the heel on the floor. Then, fully extend the hips in this position (See Fig. 164). Hold the stretch for 10 to 60 seconds. Then, lower the hips, reverse the foot positioning, and repeat the stretch on the other side.

Fig. 164

EXERCISE GOAL: The goal of this exercise is to challenge flexibility in the hip flexor and quadriceps groups, as well as kneeling balance and core stabilization.

SETUP AND ALIGNMENT: Stand behind the BOSU. Lower one knee to the center of the dome. Then step forward in front of the dome with the opposite leg in a lunge position. Align the hip of the back leg directly over the knee, and the knee of the front leg directly over, or slightly behind, the ankle. Place the hands on the hips.

PERFORMING THE EXERCISE: Shift the body forward, slowly extending the hip of the leg that is on the dome. The front knee can move slightly forward of the ankle (See Fig. 165). Perform a posterior pelvic tilt to enhance the stretch. Hold this active/passive stretch for 10 to 60 seconds. Then, return to the starting position, change legs, and repeat the stretch on the other side.

Fig. 165

SAFETY CONSIDERATIONS: Keep the front knee between the first and fifth toes throughout the stretch. Do not hyperextend the lumbar spine while lunging forward. Instead, maintain neutral lumbar posture, or a posterior pelvic tilt. The toes of the back foot may rest on the floor for balance assistance, or may be lifted for more balance challenge.

VARIATIONS AND COMMENTS: For more flexibility, balance and stabilization challenge, place the front foot further forward and lunge more deeply into the stretch. Place the hands on the front thigh (See Fig. 166). Perform a posterior pelvic tilt to enhance the stretch. For more quadriceps stretch, flex the knee of the back leg, lifting the heel toward the hips. You may assist the movement passively by grasping the foot with the same side hand and drawing it toward the same side gluteal muscle. Hold this active/passive stretch for 10 to 60 seconds. Then, return to the starting position, change legs, and repeat the stretch on the other side.

Fig. 166

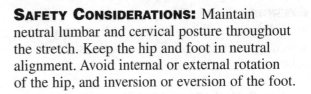

EXERCISE GOAL: The goal of this exercise is to challenge flexibility in the gastrocnemius and soleus, as well as standing balance and core stabilization.

SETUP AND ALIGNMENT: Stand upright, approximately 12 to 18 inches behind the BOSU. Place the hands on the hips.

PERFORMING THE EXERCISE: Step forward with one foot, placing the heel close to the platform and the toes up against the dome. Slide the heel in closer, allowing the toes to lift higher on the dome, until a stretch is felt in the calf region (See Fig. 167). Hold this passive stretch for 10 to 60 seconds. Then, return to the starting position, change legs, and repeat the stretch on the other side.

SAFETY CONSIDERATIONS: Maintain neutral lumbar and cervical posture throughout the stretch. Keep the hip and foot in neutral alignment. Avoid internal or external rotation of the hip, and inversion or eversion of the foot.

VARIATIONS AND COMMENTS: For more flexibility challenge, hold the foot against the dome and perform a full body lean. Simultaneously, actively dorsi flex the ankle to enhance the stretch (See Fig. 168). Hold this stretch for 10 to 60 seconds. Then, return to the starting position, change legs, and repeat the stretch on the other side.

Fig. 168

Fig. 167

EXERCISE GOAL: The goal of this exercise is to challenge flexibility in the tibialis anterior and anterior compartment group, as well as standing balance and core stabilization.

SETUP AND ALIGNMENT: Stand with the back of the body facing the dome. The heels should be placed approximately 12 inches from the platform. Lift one foot, flex the knee, and place the top of the foot on the dome with the toes pointing back. Slightly flex or "soften" the knee of the weight bearing leg. Rest the hands on the hips.

PERFORMING THE EXERCISE: Slowly shift the body forward, directing the knee over the toes. Gently press the ankle of the back leg down toward the dome until a stretch is felt in the front of the lower leg (See Fig. 169). To enhance the stretch, while pressing the ankle down simultaneously envision drawing the BOSU forward. Hold this stretch for 10 to 60 seconds. Then, return to the starting position and repeat the stretch on the other side.

Fig. 169

SAFETY CONSIDERATIONS: Keep the front knee between the first and fifth toes throughout the stretch. Do not hyperextend the lumbar spine while lunging forward. Instead, maintain neutral lumbar posture.

VARIATIONS AND COMMENTS: For more flexibility challenge, bend the supporting leg until the back knee is flexed approximately 90 degrees. Simultaneously, actively plantar flex the ankle of the back leg to enhance the stretch (See Fig. 170). Hold this stretch for 10 to 60 seconds. Then, return to the starting position, change legs, and repeat the stretch on the other side.

Fig. 170

SAMPLE BOSU PROGRAMMING MODULES

Following are examples of movement sequences or modules that can be performed on the BOSU Balance Trainer. For additional reference, these modules are demonstrated with music and cueing on the companion "BOSU Integrated Balance Training" video.

MODULE I – WARM-UP AND ACCLIMATION

MOUNT AND DISMOUNT: Facing side, walk over top. Facing front, walk sideways over top. Pause on top. Step off to the back.

STEP-UPS: Step up, up, down, down with walk or jog. Hold on top.

DOUBLE LEG BALANCE: Practice "centered position" and level feet.

DOUBLE LEG BALANCE WITH HEAD MOVEMENT: Turn head R, then L. Tip head R, then L. Close eyes. Count to 5 or 10. Open eyes.

DOUBLE LEG BALANCE WITH VISUAL TRACKING: Move arms side and overhead. Follow arm movement with eyes.

ALTERNATING COMPRESSIONS: Build to walk, march and jog.

DYNAMIC BALANCE: Squat with reaching and pulling arms. Squat with trunk rotation. Touch outside of knees, calves, ankles or dome.

COMPRESSIONS TO DOUBLE LEG BOUNCE: Build to 3x bouncing, 1x jump-stick.

JUMP-STICK: Alternate with compressions.

SINGLE LEG BALANCE: Toe touch side, then lift leg side. Repeat both sides.

COMPRESSIONS TO RELIEVE FOOT/ANKLE TENSION.

COMPRESSIONS: Center body on dome.

SIDE-SQUAT LUNGES: Alternate sides. Vary to 1x side squat lunge, 1x squat on top of dome. Vary squat on top of dome to squat with rotation, alternating sides. Vary squat with rotation to jump-stick 2x.

SIDE-TAP LUNGES: Vary cadence and range of motion.

COMPRESSIONS TO STEP-UPS: Begin by stepping down, down, up, up. Hold on top.

SINGLE LEG BALANCE: Hold leg side or move front, side and back. Step-ups to transition to balance on other leg.

LEAPS: Vary step-ups to leaps. Perform from the back or side of the dome. Hold and balance on one leg at the top of each leap. Change sides. Step down to kneeling position.

SINGLE KNEE BALANCE: Bent-knee side lift, or straight-leg side lift. Hold and balance. Change sides. Lower to kneeling position with hands on floor.

OPPOSITE ARM/LEG RAISE: Lift opposite arm and leg. Progress to pulling knee and elbow into core, then back to balanced position. Alternate sides. Come up to standing position.

COMPRESSIONS: Center body on dome.

SIDE-TAP LUNGES: Vary cadence and range of motion. Alternate sides, traveling clockwise and counter-clockwise around dome. Vary side-tap lunges to "air lunges," where foot doesn't touch the ground.

COMPRESSIONS: Progress to step off dome and turn platform side up.

HIGH-PLANK DRILLS: Hold high-plank position. Pump legs, jog or high-knee run in place. Alternate side lunges or diagonal jumps toward the platform.

PLATFORM PUSH-UPS: Bent or straight legs.

POSTERIOR TRUNK STRETCH: Flex lumbar spine with hands on platform, hips pulling back toward heels. Turn to dome side up. Step up to compressions.

SQUAT/JUMP-STICK: Hold squat, then jump-stick. Hold squat and perform alternating compressions. Step off dome to seated position.

V-SIT: One or both legs lifted. Add counter rotation of legs and trunk with hands on dome or arms lifted.

SUPINE BALANCE: Lower to supine balance position and hold. Pull in knees and curl up to sitting position.

SEATED POSTERIOR TRUNK STRETCH: Roll trunk forward into "turtle" position and hold.

HAMSTRINGS/CALF STRETCH: Sit with one leg extended. Lean forward into stretch. Change sides and repeat.

ANTERIOR TRUNK STRETCH: Lie back over dome with knees and hips flexed or extended. Open arms side.

SUPINE TRUNK CURLS: Incline or parallel. Progress to trunk curl with simultaneous pelvic tilt.

SUPINE BRIDGE: Both feet on floor or one leg up. Progress to active spinal extension in bridge position. Extend spine a few degrees. Then, return to neutral.

SUPINE OPPOSITE ARM/LEG RAISE: Balance on one side. Then, change sides and repeat. Pull knees toward chest and roll to seated position.

SEATED ROTARY TRUNK STRETCH: Rotate trunk to one side, then the other.

LATERAL TRUNK FLEXION: Bent knee or straight leg position. Vary to lateral trunk flexion with abduction of the top leg.

SIDELYING BALANCE: Elbow on floor or both arms up. Balance with the legs and trunk parallel to the floor. Repeat lateral trunk flexion, abduction and lateral balance on the other side. Roll to seated position.

SEATED WALK-AROUNDS: Move around dome in both directions. Turn to prone position.

PRONE SPINAL EXTENSION: Hands on thighs, at forehead or overhead. Vary to prone spinal extension with alternating side rotation.

PRONE BALANCE: Legs lifted with hands on floor, to the side or overhead. Hold and balance.

PRONE ARM/LEG FLUTTER: Flutter legs only, or both arms and legs. Vary to flutter with hip tilt from side to side.

POSTERIOR TRUNK STRETCH: Drape over dome with arms on legs or overhead.

ALTERNATING LEG FORWARD LUNGES: From floor to dome. Vary to forward lunge with trunk rotation. Rotate trunk toward lunging leg. Step up on dome to compressions.

SIDE SQUAT LUNGES: Press 4x into squat on one side, then lift over dome and repeat other side. Decrease reps to pressing 2x, then singles.

BACK-TAP LUNGES: Alternate legs with single lunges. Step down to kneeling position.

KNEELING BALANCE WITH CROSS-TOUCH: Kneel on one or both knees and reach one arm across the body toward the floor.

KNEELING HIP FLEXOR STRETCH: Step forward with one leg from kneeling position on dome. Hold stretch. Repeat both sides. Stand and face dome from the side.

STEP-UPS: Walking or jogging, travel halfway around the dome in one direction. Then, change sides. Step up to compressions.

JUMP DRILLS: Perform 45, 90 and 180 degree jump turns. Repeat both directions.

CROSS-COUNTRY SKI JUMPS: Alternate the legs forward and back on top of the dome. Vary with twisting jumps with alternating torso rotation "mogul jumps." Compressions. Then, step down to prone position.

PRONE HIP EXTENSION: Alternating single leg or double leg extension. Vary to simultaneous arm thrust (without spinal extension).

PRONE BALANCE WITH OPPOSITE HEEL TOUCH: Bend one knee and reach for the heel with the opposite arm. Alternate sides. Walk hands forward in prone position until knees and lower thighs are centered on dome.

PIKE-UPS: Pike with elbows on floor or hands on floor. Vary to single leg lift at top of pike. Turn into supine position.

SUPINE BICYCLE: Small range of motion with knees bent or full range with legs and arms fully extended.

ROTARY TORSO STRETCH: Slide hips off dome and onto floor. Rest legs on dome and rotate legs to one side, torso to the other. Repeat other side.

CARDIO KICKBOXING: Begin with knee lift from floor to dome. Progress to knee lift/front kick.

OVER THE DOME: Step up, jump-stick, step down to the other side. Repeat, then hold on opposite side and repeat cardio kickboxing combo on the other side.

COMPRESSIONS: Center body on dome.

STRADDLE KNEE LIFTS: With or without propulsion. Vary knee lift to side lift, front kick and jump-stick.

COMPRESSIONS: Center body on dome.

BACK-TAP LUNGES: Vary cadence and range of motion. Alternate compressions with back-tap lunges. Step off the back, onto the floor.

ALTERNATING KNEE LIFTS: With or without propulsion. Vary to repeater knee lifts with and without propulsion.

STANDING ABDUCTION: Single leg balance on top of dome. Abduct one leg for multiple reps, then change legs. Step off dome and come to sidelying position.

LATERAL HIP LIFT: Bent or straight legs. Progress to lateral hip lift with abduction at top of movement. Repeat both sides. Then, roll to supine position on dome.

ROTARY TRUNK BALANCE: Bent or extended top leg. Rotate trunk both directions with each leg. Then, switch legs. Roll to seated position and turn BOSU to platform side up position.

PLATFORM TILTS: Bent or straight legs. Tilt front and back or side to side. Vary to tilts with alternating leg lifts.

LUNGING HIP FLEXOR STRETCH: Step with outside leg toward dome. Hold lunge with back leg either bent or straight. Repeat other side.

PLATFORM BALANCE: Sit on platform with crossed legs. Hold and balance.